How to manage

care homes an

(over 90 policies a

MW00773692

ABUSE	UNDERSTA. DEATH
ACTIVITIES	INFECTION
DEMENTIA	FIRE
FIRST AID	FOOD HYGIENE
MANUAL HANDLING	MEDICATION
MENTAL ILLNESS	HEALTH Health and Safety & SAFETY

By

James Safo

Entrepreneur)BA(Hons), Psy.N, GN, Cert. Ed, Cert Acct, Dip H&S, RMA, AI, VI, Cert. business Certifiers Aid, Food hygiene.

1

Quick search

Chapters with subheading.

James Safo's right as the researcher, author, designer of this publication to be identified and respected in accordance with the Copyright, Designs and Patent's Act 1988.

All Rights Reserved

Disclaimer (Exclusive clause)

The author and all employees disclaim any incorrect interpretation wrong answers to questions or text, harm include emotional, psychological, and physical or any form of harm to the reader/listener or being given information by third parties.

Furthermore, this disclaimer protects all contributory people, directors, employees, 3rd party, and author and will not be liable for any injury caused. Please check where you are in doubt as policies changes evolve

Dedication

I dedicate this book to all my children who suffered with me and still we remain strong and united.

Acknowledgements

The real author of all my books is Almighty God/Allah/Parama Nandha who through his messengers. I was not capable of neither writing books or achieving those high-powered qualifications: physically, 75% of my bones are in the advanced stage of arthritis, I have the worst type of cardiovascular disease, a large heart (hypertrophy), chronic depression and anxiety and, worst of all, three out of four of my brain lobes have been damaged since 1998 as a result of a serious car accident. Yet I rose to be one of the most successful international entrepreneurs in the world, miscarriage stripped my millions, and now come back to be more than what I had.

Preface

As a qualified psychiatric and General trained nurse, BA (Hons) law and account) etc, and having own about ten (include 6 care homes at one stage) business at the same time in United Kingdom for over twenty-five years. I hope this book " policies and procedure in healthcare" together with my other book "care homes: staff training" and "how to set up care homes" will give more insight to prospective proprietor and employee, similarly, is to provide knowledge and understanding of care the public expect from the healthcare staff.

About the Author

I was an abandon child at the age of four. As an adult I became a high-profile international entrepreneur in United Kingdom for over twenty-five years and owned ten different businesses at the same time, including an international college, and at one stage owe about 6 care homes at the same time. I wrote all document needed to set up and manage them successful. etc. I was arguably one of the most successful businessmen in Europe at the time, I am now author of over twenty-six books of which some have been translated to Arabic, Chinese, French and Spanish. I am strong believer of Almighty God and his messengers, include Jesus Christ, Prophet Muhammad, Krishna and the ten Gurus

My areas of Qualification

LLM(Master of Law o/g)

Legal researcher (master level)

Business, CSR and business human Right (master level)

1. BA (Hons) , Law: include Criminal, Tort, damages, Contract, Property, Equity and Trust,

European law, Public, Constitutional, Judicial Review

2. On Master of Law level; which is on -going, but I have passed the module " legal research", and "business, CSR Corporate social responsibility and human Right law"

3. Advance Dip. Business Law, Level 4: include Employment, Agency, Damages, Tort, Contract, employment tribunal etc.

4. Dip. Criminology

5. BA (Hons)op. Account: Financial Accountant and Management Accountant

6. Cert. Acct; Professional Certificate in Financial and Management Accounting

7. Dip. Book-keeping, Level 3

8. Nursing: RMN Psychiatry trained nurse

9. General Trained Nurse

10. Cert. in Education (Lecturer)

11. Business Certificate in Advanced Management

12. Cert. Business Enterprise

13. Advanced Food Hygiene

14. Intermediate Health and Safety

15. Dip. Safety Management

16. International Entrepreneur for over 25 years

17. Computers: Cert. Cisco Level 2 Technician, (build, repair, networking)

18. Dip. Clait Plus (in all software)

19. New Clait Dip. Level 2

20. Microsoft Specialist

21. ECDL Level 2

22. Script writing: Dip. TV, radio, stage and film

23. Non-fiction writing: Dip. Autobiography, Biography and Family History

24. Cert. in Counselling

25. Author/Self-Publisher: Over 12 books (with some yet to be published)

26. Plumbing: Level 3 City and Guild

27. Theology: Cert. Bible studies; researched Theology for my PhD (most faiths)

28. Psychology and Social Science (Level 1 at university)

29. Photographer: Portrait, Glamour and Figure Photographer (PGFP).

30. Dip. Hypnotherapy

31. National Vocation Qualification (NVQ); Internal Verifier, Trainer and Assessor

32. 2018-2020: University Student of LLM (Master of Laws) NVQ

33. Author Publisher of over 22 titles books by June 2019

CONTENT

9

Application for employment form

or residential home

initial action, appeal

employee representative

mode of appeal, training

complaints, personal details

Dying, death and bereavement

Procedure care of the dying

Objective, advice

procedure for death

definition of death

signs, procedure

what to do after a bereavement

what to do in all religion

death at home or in hospital

registering a death

cremation, burial

Christian, Judaism

Funerals, Hinduism

post-mortem and organ transplants

procedure at death

Conscious adults

Unconscious adults

Adults, Respiration;

Shock; Anaphylactic shock

Guidelines to completing

resident review form

reviews, dental needs

optician; chiropody

religious needs;

 day care/activities

unfulfilled ambitions; social and

 family contacts

physical health;

 psychological/mental health

list of present medication,

 reviews medication

personal finance and expenditure, clothing

which floor?

17

Types of Interview

Skills of Interviewer

aim, questions

Intruders

procedure for loss

of mains

gas leak or loss,

water (loss or flooding)

what to do in the event of loss of water

planned repairs by water board (loss of water

flooding,

electricity (loss of)

Job description: manager

aim of post, key tasks

function, communication and liaison

fire, education

staffing, information

stocktaking, meetings

employing staff, routines

staff appraisal

TERMS OF CONDITIONS

OF EMPLOYMENT

Remuneration, criminal records bureau

annual leave, maternity leave

how to get SMP, paternity leave

eligibility, sick pay

references, documents

training, termination

routine, valuables

staff / team meetings

code of conduct

smoking, policy

confidentiality

25

What Is A "Vulnerable" Adult?

Who Might abuse Someone?

Defining "Abuse",

Types of Abuse

Types of Physical Abuse

Types of Sexual Abuse

Types of Emotional Abuse

Types of Financial Abuse

Types of Institutional Abuse

Types of Discriminatory Abuse

Responses:

Neglect by others

Neglect is;

Physical Neglect

Emotional Neglect

11- point communication programme

Chapter 1

ABUSE AND ADULT PROTECTION

This policy has been devised with reference to the Department of Health guidance 2000.

Definition

A vulnerable adult is someone aged 18 or over, who may be at risk because of a mental, physical or learning disability as well as age or illness and cannot always take care of themselves or protect themselves against harm or exploitation.

Abuse can be discriminatory, financial, neglect, physical, psychological, sexual and verbal and can happen anywhere and to anyone.

Abuse is a violation of an individual's human and civil rights by any other person or persons. Abuse may consist of a single act or repeated acts.

It may be:

Physical	Hitting, Slapping, pushing, restraining
Psychological	Blaming, swearing, humiliation, harassing, threats
Neglect	Failure to provide appropriate food, shelter, clothing, medical

Abuse of Individual Rights	Isolation, invasion of privacy, restricted access, discouraging sexual relationships, racial abuse, administering medicines against their will, e.g. by disguising medicines in client's food or drink.
Professional Abuse	Failure to act on suspected crime/abuse, poor care practice, resource shortfalls, shortage of staff.
Sexual	Direct or indirect involvement in sexual activity without consent. Coercion to touch, e.g. breasts, genitals. Looking at indecent images, exposure, harassment, sexual innuendo or teasing.
Financial	Theft of money, valuables, forging signatures on cheques or falsifying documents for personal

	gain.
Bullying	This can be physical or emotional and classed as abuse. Residents that persistently bully others may be asked to leave the Home following a review in the presence of Care Managers, relatives or CPN.
Discriminatory Abuse	• Lack of respect shown to an individual • Unrealistic expectations of a person's ability • Signs of a sub-standard service offered to an individual • Repeated exclusion from rights afforded to citizens such as health, education, employment, criminal justice and civic status. • All behaviour or medical symptoms explained solely in terms or the person's disability • Lack of consideration for

individual diversity e.g.
race, culture and ethnicity,
age, gender, religion,
disability, sexuality

Indicators of Institutional Abuse

Everyone has the right to feel safe and be treated with respect by all health and social care organisations. This includes volunteers and staff employed within those organisations. Institutional Abuse is mistreatment or abuse by a regime or the individuals within an institution. Institutional abuse occurs when the routines, systems and norms of an institution take precedence over the preferred lifestyle and cultural diversity of the residents in its care.

Institutional abuse can include:

- Inappropriate or poor care
- Misuse of medication e.g. sedating residents to make life easier for the care staff

31

- Inappropriate use of restraint and/or methods of restraint
- Denial of visitors or phone calls
- Restricted access to toilet or bathing facilities
- Restricted access to appropriate medical or social care

- Failure to ensure appropriate privacy or personal dignity
- Lack of flexibility and choice, e.g. mealtimes and bedtimes, choice of food
- Lack of personal clothing or possessions
- Lack of privacy
- Lack of adequate procedures, e.g. for medication, financial management, restraint, sexuality
- Controlling relationships between staff and residents
- Repeated acts of poor professional practice

Managers and staff should ensure that the operation of the service is centred on the needs of the residents and not on those of the institution. The systems in place to ensure the smooth running of the institution should be flexible, residents can become abusive if they are dogmatic and non-negotiable. Managers should ensure that there are mechanisms in place that both maintain and review the appropriateness, quality and impact of the service for which they are responsible. These mechanisms should take the view of the Residents and their carers into account at all times.

Aims of the Care establishment

- The Management will conduct the establishment in a manner to which promotes clients rights, dignity, privacy and beliefs of all the individuals concerned and does not discriminate on the basis of race, colour, culture, religion, language, gender, age, disability or sexual orientation.
- All vulnerable adults have a right to be protected and their decisions respected even if that decision involves risk.
- Everyone will be treated sensitively at all stages of the investigation.

- Vulnerable adults who have been abused need the same care and sensitivity as the alleged abuser.
- The responsibility to refer the vulnerable adult thought to be at risk rests with the person who has the concerns.
- All agencies receiving confidential information in the context of a vulnerable adult investigation will make decisions about sharing this information in appropriate circumstances.
- Vulnerable adults have the right to have an independent advocate if they wish at any stage of the investigation.

To minimize the risk of abuse of residents by staff, managers will carry out stringent procedures regarding references, staff work history and checking name, POVA register and Criminal Records Bureau checks.

The Home's policy must aim to prevent any form of abuse to residents or staff.

All staff are accountable for their own actions or lack of action. All incidents of abuse (including neglect as per Mental Capacity Act 2005) will be reported to the police for investigation which may result in criminal proceedings.

Staff must record any bruises or signs of possible abuse and report it immediately to the Manager or Person on Call.

Where a person knows or has cause for concern that a vulnerable adult has been abused or may be a victim of a crime there is a duty to inform the local Social Services Department and police.

Any staff suspected of any form of abuse will be instantly suspended pending an investigation. Details of such an allegation should be documented immediately. The member of staff should not be given details of the allegation. This cannot be dealt with by an internal investigation within the Home. The borough's Community Care Team and the service user's placing authority should be informed in accordance with (Surrey Multi Agency Procedures February 2005) where a decision will be made within 4 hours as to who will lead the investigation.

All staff will have to undertake training on abuse and adult protection both in service and external training.

Chapter 2

ACCIDENT PROCEDURE IN THE HOME

When a resident has an accident:

1. First call other staff member for help (do not leave resident) and delegate.

2. Carry out visual observation of the casualty and the immediate environment to make sure it is safe for you to give him/her first aid (e.g., casualty may be attached to live electric cable).

3. Quickly assess resident and note the signs and symptoms which might lead to you carrying out a first aider's diagnosis. Seek casualty's permission before administering first aid (unless unconscious).

4. Administer appropriate first aid. Remember to keep talking to casualty during the process of first aid.

5. If necessary notify the doctor but if your initial diagnosis is emergency call the ambulance straight away and continue your first aid until they arrive. All head injuries must be reported to the doctor/GP on-call whatever

the time it is since concussion may occur hours later after an accident.

6. Ask the other staff to write down information about the resident to be given to the ambulance when they arrive. Complete transfer to hospital form.

7. If possible arrange an escort. A full written report of the accident with medical history, next of kin, present medication and a completed body map are to accompany client. If there is time to complete, if not ring A&E Department after client has left in ambulance.

8. Do not waste valuable time, e.g. unless you need advice, inform manager or on call staff after resident being seen to.

9. Complete record in accident book.

10. Notify designated care manager. If the resident does not have a care manager notify the placing authorities duty manager.

11. Reporting of injuries, diseases and dangerous occurrences as follows: If the

accident is reportable under (RIDDOR) complete a Form 2508.

12. Inform the Environmental Health Department by telephoning within 24 hours of the accident occurring and send a copy of the Form 2508 to each of those offices, retaining the third copy to be filed in the home.

   a. Fractures of skull, spine, pelvis, bone of wrist or arm, ankle or leg. But not a bone in the hand or foot.

   b. Amputation of hand, foot, finger or toe.

   c. Loss of sight

   d. Chemical or hot metal burn to the eye or any penetrating injury to the eye

   e. Injury resulting from an electric shock or electrical burn leading to unconsciousness, or requiring resuscitation; or requiring admittance to hospital for more than 24 hours.

   f. Unconsciousness caused by asphyxia or exposure to harmful substances or biological agent

   g. Acute illness requiring medical treatment, or loss of consciousness arising from absorption of any substance by inhalation, ingestion or through the skin

   h. Acute illness requiring medical treatment where there is reason to believe that this resulted from exposure to a biological agent or its toxins or infected material.

13. Record in full in the resident's Care Notes and if necessary addition is made to the care plan.

14. Inform the next of kin and next of kin must be notified within 24 hours and the person whom you spoke to must be entered in the accident report and the daily care notes. Ask client to countersign accident book if they are unable to or refuse to sign staff to countersign. If client stated they do not want next of kin notified, this must be documented in the accident book and also noted in the care notes. Relatives who state they do not want to be informed of minor accidents must be recorded in the client's care plan. All accidents involving chemicals, staff are to follow the first aid procedures from the COSHH data sheets. If a per son seeks medical attention, a copy of the data sheet should be taken to the medics.

15. If the person does not need hospital care or is returned from casualty continue observation for at least 48 hours.

16. An incident form must be completed. If the client has a CPN and a care manager they must also be notified. The person you spoke to and time must be written in the care notes and the incident book. If they do not have a CPN then the Duty Care Manager of the placing authority e.g. Croydon, Bromley or Richmond must be notified ensuring you record the person's name and time of call.

17. All incidents of violence must be reported to CSCI (recording the name and time again in the incident book and care notes).

18. Report to GP and if client does not have a psychiatrist, request a referral back to one. Record feedback from GP in documents above.

In Cases Involving Staff/Visitors:

1. Deliver appropriate first aid care.

2. Summon emergency ambulance service if necessary.

3. Notify next of kin (staff).

4. Complete accident report in Accident Book.

5. Complete notifiable injury form (F2508) if applicable as listed in number 10 above.

Chapter 3

ADMISSION & DISCHARGE PROCEDURE

Prospective residents may be referred via Care Managers or next of kin, Doctor, Social Workers or self usually via a telephone conversation. When an emergency admission is made the registered person undertakes to inform the Service user within 48 hours about key aspects, rules and routines of the Home and to have a detailed care plan. We aim to meet the rest of the admission criteria within 5 working days, which would include the Homes Terms and Conditions.

Unplanned admissions are avoided where possible.

The person taking the call will ask general questions e.g. name of person, age, next of kin, diagnosis and care required at present. A contact telephone number will be taken. An appointment is made for the prospective resident to view the home. An assessment of the resident's needs may also be done at this time. (It is helpful if the

Care Manager forwards their assessment prior to viewing). The person from the Home preparing the assessment needs to consider that:-

1.   The resident meets the registration certificate

2.   that the Home can provide the necessary care

3.   that the resident will "fit in" with existing clients

4.   Comply with admission criteria

Prospective Service Users will be given the opportunity to meet the Manager/Keyworker in their own home or current situation is different.

The prospective client will be shown the relevant empty bedroom, all communal areas and introduced to the other residents. If the person wishes they may choose to spend a few hours or a day at the Home. Any questions they may have about the Home should be able to be answered. The person may visit alone, escorted by their Care Manager or by their next of kin whichever the client chooses. The person may also be seen in the hospital or at their home. All prospective clients will be assessed against the Homes admission criteria.

A decision of whether to be admitted to the Home does not have to be made that day. Usually up to a period of a week is given. The prospective resident has to agree to admission - not the next of kin or the Care Manager alone, unless the person is under a Guardianship Order. All prospective clients should be offered a brochure or service users guide.

At the time of assessment it should be explained that all residents are admitted on a 4-6-week trial basis (this period may be extended if both parties agree) so as to:

a)   allow the resident to decide whether he/she would like to reside at the home;

b)   for the Home to feel comfortable that it can meet their needs;

c)   a care plan should be ready for the client before admission

Admission Day

The client will usually be brought to the Home by their Care Manager or next of kin. Luggage etc. will be brought to their bedroom. Tea or coffee will be offered, and the client will be introduced to their keyworker. The keyworker will explain their role. The client may either choose to spend time in their room or sit with other residents whilst they have a drink. The call bell, fire procedure, residents' noticeboard and menu board will be explained. It is also stated that the resident has free access to the kitchen.

The council contract and/or Home's contract is then completed and signed. Copies of both will be given to the residents. A property inventory (including valuables) is also made in the presence and signed by the client. There will be 3 copies one for the clients file, one for the client and one to remain in the book. A 6-week review date is set.

All valuables including jewellery, cash, cheque, building society books and bank cards etc must be recorded in the property book. If the client wishes to retain these valuables, they must sign the relevant book to state this.

Items which the client wishes the Home to keep in the Home's safe must be entered into the safe book with details of each item – cheque book must be documented, and the name of the bank must be recorded as well. What cheque number the cheque book begins with and the cheque numbers of the last cheque. Bank cards must state the start date and the end date. The client and witness must sign the safe book and a receipt with the items listed must be given to the client. A duplicate copy is to be kept in the receipt book.

The keyworker will also complete the following paperwork:-

1. An Admission Sheet

2. A Medicine Record

3. Care Notes (front sheet) with details or any medical history

4. Name and details to be entered in Residents Register

5. If the resident is the change GP, this form needs to be completed

6. Reordered medicines to be counted

7. Risk Assessment - all clients must have a manual handling and financial risk
      assessment.

8. Care plan

9.	Complete weight chart and record height

Throughout the trial period the Care Manager, and/or CPN will be in contact, day care may be arranged. The keyworker should ensure that all queries are dealt with and discussed with the Manager and other relevant parties.

At the six-week review, the resident, next of kin (if resident wishes), Care Manager, keyworker, Manager of the Home, CPN and other relevant professionals may be invited. Any grievances or queries will try to be resolved. If the resident is happy to reside at the Home then the case is usually closed by the Care Manager. The multi-disciplinary team will continue to meet the resident's needs. A 6-month formal review will be held by the Home thereafter and then annually.

Emergency Admission

If a prospective client wishes to be admitted on an emergency basis, the manager must obtain the following information first:

1)	A full history of the clients detailed, and needs must be documented and assessed against the homes admission criteria.

2)	A copy of the care manager's assessment will be requested.

3) If possible the client or their advocate should visit the home first, or the manager should visit where the client is presently living.

If the manager agrees that the home may be able to meet the prospective client's needs, an admission may take place. A full assessment must take place within 48 hours. The placement will only be agreed on a one-week trial basis for both parties.

Discharge of Client

If a client needs cannot be met within the Home of the client wishes to leave the following procedures will occur.

A review meeting will be arranged. All interested parties i.e. the client, next of kin, care manager, CPN etc, will be invited (as per clients consent) to discuss future accommodation.

Four to six weeks' notice from either party needs to be given in writing.

When an alternative placement is found and on the day of discharge the home will have completed a transfer form which will have all the details of medication, next of kin etc.

Discharge at Short Notice: Self Discharge

As per discharge policy above:

If a client wishes to leave we will need:

1) Notice from the advocate (Next of kin placing authority)

2) The On-Duty staff will dissuade client to leave until the right arrangements have been made. The client needs to put in writing that they are discharging themselves against advice by giving reason (if she wants).

3) Request client to give the home a forwarding address (if he/she wishes).

4) Client to be made aware that we will notify the next of kin, placing authority and National Care Standards Commission etc.

5) Client to made aware that if the home feels that their action is dangerous to themselves and others e.g. mentally unstable the police will be informed.

6) The home will not physically restrain the client from leaving.

7) All property and valuables to be recorded in the property with a witness and the client or advocates signature.

Emergency Admission of Service Users.

Admissions of an urgent nature are only permitted in instances where the welfare of the individual might be harmed if the admission is delayed. Therefore it is possible to admit a service user without a full assessment being carried out.

In these circumstances as much information as possible must be obtained within 48 hours.

It will be stated in the emergency agreement, that the admission is short term only and that any decision for the placement to become long term would not be made until a full assessment and review had been completed.

ADMISSION CRITERIA FOR (MENTAL HEALTH)

1. Mental Health clients must have a Mental Health diagnosis of a functional nature i.e. psychosis or neurosis for example Schizophrenia, Bi-polar Affective Disorder, Depression or Anxiety and have elderly needs.

2. Admission is provided regardless of religion, race, colour, marital status, sexual preference or national origin. Cultural needs will be assessed and met if able. Discussion prior to admission will take place and advice sought elsewhere if necessary.

3. Admission to the rest home is voluntary. No one can be admitted to the Home against his/her will unless under a local authority Guardianship Order. There is no entrance fee. Monthly fees are payable one month in advance. The proposed resident and/or his/her agent or next of kin are encouraged to visit the Home.

4. (i) The resident will only be assessed if he/she likes the Home.

(ii) The person will be assessed by either the manager or senior staff (see assessment form). If there are medical concerns, a Doctor will be asked to carry out an assessment. The application process will only commence if the resident wishes to be admitted and the Home accepts him/her.

5. The services of the Home are provided to meet the needs of the residents. Admission is subject to binding in the contract.

6. Must need residential and not nursing care.

7. Clients who have incontinence will be assessable via main stairs and an 8-person (wheel chair) passenger lift.

8. All diets including medical, cultural and individual preferences can be catered for upon prior arrangement.

9. All prospective clients will be assessed as to whether they will 'fit in' with existing residents.

10. Any physical or mental deterioration in existing residents will be re-assessed regularly so as to ensure the Home can continue to meet their needs. If the prospective resident is experiencing any medical condition of an infectious or contagious nature the Management reserves the right to assess each case individually at any time and refuse admission to the Home.

11. The home will not admit clients who have a history (within the last 5 years) of physical violence

Chapter 4

ACCIDENT/INCIDENT FORM FOR RESIDENTS AND STAFF

Particulars of Resident/Staff

Name _____ Mr/Mrs/Miss

Date of Birth _____ GP __

Particulars of Accident/Incident

Date of Accident/Incident _____ Time

Location *(or room no if applicable)*

Description of Accident/Injury or Incident

How did it happen?

If apparatus or equipment involved - specify type

How did it contribute to the accident/incident

Name(s) of Witness*(s)* (*if applicable*)

Staff on duty:

1. Doctor Informed

      YES/NO   NAME:

      _____TIME:

2. Care Manager Informed

      YES/NO   NAME:

      _____TIME:

3. Relatives Informed

      YES/NO   NAME: TIME:

4. Person on-call Informed

      YES/NO   NAME: TIME:

5. C.S.C.I – Fax: 02082566466

      YES/NO   NAME:_____TIME:

6. Psychiatrist

      YES/NO   NAME:_____TIME:

7. District Nurse

      YES/NO   NAME:_____TIME:

8. Body Map

      YES/NO   NAME:_____TIME:

9. Adult Protection - Fax: 02084071376

      YES/NO   NAME:_____TIME:

10. Police - 02086671212 (999 Emergency)

      YES/NO   NAME:_____TIME:

Has an F2508 form been completed? YES/NO. If Yes, date sent to the Health and Safety Officer _____and date sent to The Commission For Social Care Inspection Unit

ACTION TAKEN

Signed by Witness (*if applicable*) _____ Date _

Signed by Person Completing Form ____ Date _

Signed by Person in Charge ____Date

Chapter 5

AIMS & OBJECTIVES

To run the Home to a very high standard and give effective environmental, physical and psychological care for the elderly, incorporating quality job satisfaction and status to the people it employs. Reliably serving the community as a whole by providing an established care home for eighteen elderly people, who have a past or present functional mental illness, which has its roots in respect, dignity, independence and flexibility for choice, rights and fulfillment. All prospective residents will be assessed against our admission criteria.

To promote a high standard of care and to safeguard and protect the interest and welfare of the residents by ensuring that all services adhere to:

a)   The Home Policies

 b)   National Care Standards

c)   Home-Life Code of Practice

d)   Homes are for Living in

e)   The Department of Health's Guidance documents and circulars

f)   National Care Standards

g)   Careers Code of Contact

It is our aim to offer our residents the opportunity to enjoy their quality of life by providing their needs including a safe, manageable and comfortable environment (physically, emotionally and psychologically).

To incorporate good business practice in our dealing with residents, their relatives, staff, members of the public and their servants. All are welcome to visit between 9.00 am and 9.00 pm, unless prior arrangements are made.

Continually stimulate the residents by giving priority to hobbies and interests and endeavor to enable them to pursue these individually or in a group. Encourage integration into the community and to continue activities outside the Home.

Enlist the services of the various and numerous organizations which come into the Home to provide entertainment, talks, discussions, demonstrations, library service and visitors to the home including children and caring members of the community.

Encourage staff to participate in care plans with suggestions, observations and their skills, enlisting the agreement of the residents and encouraging their predication.

We aim to improve resident's environment by avoiding institutionalization, by provision of a safe, suitable environment, which is friendly and homely, with high standards of equipment and hygiene (using local and national legislation). Encourage homely atmosphere by giving residents the choice of having their own furniture in their rooms, their possessions around them which enhances this policy and improves the quality of life.

1) We offer 24-hour staffing by experiences staff who have access to regular supervision and tuition to ensure they maintain the Warren's high standards of care.

2) The Home provides 3 comfortable communal lounges, one of which is a 24-hour smoking area. A lift serves all three floors and a medic shower is provided for residents whose mobility is restricted.

3) Fees and additional services will be discussed and agreed prior to admission, and then incorporated into the contract.

In conclusion, we aim to be at all times open-minded and receptive to suggestions from residents, next of kin, Social Services, etc., in the improvements of the home for the benefit of the residents and those working in the home.

Aims and objectives of key workers

The responsibility of key workers includes making sure that all the residents individual needs are satisfied. This includes:

1.*Stimulation and motivation* e.g. promoting indoor and outdoor activities.

2.*Physical* e.g. food, sleep, physical hygiene, clothing.

3.*Emotional* e.g. to ensure respect, choice, involvement, privacy, dignity, individuality and

    making decisions is part of the Home's routine.

4.*Sexual needs* (This needs to be taken out)

5.*Environmental* e.g. bedroom, sitting room, garden.

6. *Communication* i.e. individual, group. Spend time listening and communicating - verbally and non-verbally.

7. *Religious need.*

8. Build individual rapport /relationship without emotional involvement with the resident, the next of kin and outside agencies.

9. *Residents'* appointments e.g. dentist, optician, hospital etc. key workers must if possible escort resident.

10. Write the care notes

11. Liaison with the manager to discuss problems, needs and solution.

12. Liaison with next of kin with the permission of the resident

13. Evaluate the care plan regularly

14. Write a short biography of each resident.

15. Be prepared to answer any question from the management of official outside agencies.

PROCEDURE

(a) First prepare Biography of the resident (refer guidance) i.e., start making notes to help prepare biography in 6 weeks.

(b) Carry out assessment of the residents as per guidance note. This will help with preparation of care plan update, evaluation and review. This is done by a discussion between Key Worker, resident, manager or deputy manager. Care plan to be signed by Manager and then the Key Worker can evaluate this as often as necessary, at least once a month as per the NSC.

(c)   Assess the needs of the resident through the resident or through next of kin or friends (with resident's permission).

Chapter 6

THE SIX PRINCIPLES OF CARE

In order to ensure out residents are happy and contented, and in addition to the aims and objectives in our policy and brochure we also aim to implement the six main principles of care which are;-

Privacy, Dignity, Independence, Choice, Rights, Fulfilment

(a) - definitions taken from the book Homes Are For The Living In

(b) - further explanation to support (a)

1)Privacy;

    (a)   the right of individuals to be left alone or undisturbed and free   from intrusion or public attention into their affairs

    (b)   a place of safety - seclusion, a place of peace for one's self.

2)Dignity;

    (a)   recognition of the intrinsic value of people regardless of circumstances by respecting their uniqueness and their personal needs treating with respect

(b)   elevation of mind - to feel secure in one's self and have the   respect of others.

3)independence

(a)   opportunities to act and think without reference to another   person including a willingness to incur a degree for calculated   risk

(b)   not relying on others, thinking and acting for oneself respecting

4)Choice;

(a)   opportunity to select independently from a range of options

(b)   the power of choosing.   To select one thing from another by   one's own individual personal feeling and uniqueness as being a human being

5)Rights;

(a)   the maintenance of all entitlement associated with

citizenship

(b)   choosing in accordance with one's own identity. The   ultimate   human basic need to be able to exercise, use and understand   our needs to have power to influence our lives by using our right

6)Fulfilment

(a)   the   realisation   of   personal aspirations and abilities in all aspects of daily life

(b)   to complete, to realise completely our hopes our dreams and our aspirations

The Home Management and Staff therefore set out our objectives regarding the above mentioned which are designed as achievable and measurable standards which indicate how we are meeting our overall aim.   The Proprietor insists that all staff must respect and implement the six principles of care subject to the last two paragraphs of this document.

Privacy Objectives

1. The written admission procedure for The Home will reflect the residents right to privacy within the establishment.

2. Single bedrooms will be provided, subject to availability, for all residents except those who choose to share.

3. Locks, meeting with the specification of local authority's standard will be fitted to all bedroom doors and keys will be made available to all residents on arrival subject to residents wishes.

4. All rooms will be fitted with appropriate curtains and blinds etc to ensure a maximum of personal privacy for individual residents.

5. All residents will have uninhibited access to all communal areas including toilet and bathroom facilities and gardens, etc.

6. Staff providing personal care will demonstrate understanding and respect for the privacy of all residents by ensuring that:-
A) Toilet/bathroom doors are not left open when personal tasks of care relating to residents are being undertaken. B) Routines within The Home will never be allowed to over-ride an individual's right to privacy.

7. Night staff will not routinely check residents at night without consultation. Handover will take place in an area away from other resident.

8. Residents will be free to take their meals in their own rooms if they choose to do so. Although clients who may withdraw to their bedrooms

because they are depressed will be encouraged to socialise with others.

9. Officials and visitors will not be shown a residents bedroom without the residents specific permission.

10. All members of staff will obtain permission from residents before entering a residents bedroom.

11. Residents will have free access to their bedrooms at any time.

12. Residents will be free to entertain visitors and guests in their bedrooms.

13. All mail addressed to individual residents will be delivered unopened to residents as soon as possible after receipt.

14. All financial transactions involving residents will be conducted in private.

15. Residents will be allowed to speak to Management in privacy at any time regarding any matters of their concern.

16. Residents will be able to wash, dress, bathe and use the toilet free from intrusion.

17. Staff will adhere to confidentiality policy and not gossip about clients in and out of the Home.

Dignity Objectives

1. To address all residents in a manner of respect and respecting their individuality.

2. To provide incontinent pads and aids at all times if needed. An advisor will be offered.

3. To ensure at all times that residents when in our need are clothed correctly and that all sensory aids are offered such as false teeth, hearing aids, spectacles etc.

4. To assist any resident to the toilet facilities should they be in our need.

5. To provide where necessary a commode for overnight facilities for any resident whom may have difficulties in reaching the toilets.

6. To provide assistance by our observation to change a residents clothing when at any time of that resident's needs, respecting their privacy and dignity at all times.

7. To change bed-linens at any time day or night should a resident become incontinent.

8. To enable all residents uninhibited access to bathrooms and toilets facilities.

9. Residents will be called by the mode of address they choose and not called by nicknames.

10. Routines within The Home will never be allowed to over-ride an individual's right to their dignity.

11. To not ever dress a resident with clothing which is not of their own property, unless agreed upon by the resident involved or the relatives of that resident.

12. To ensure that when providing personal care that bathroom and toilet doors are closed at all times.

13. To ensure that when a resident is retiring to their rooms that where necessary curtains are drawn closed.

14. Mirrors will be provided in bathrooms, toilets and bedrooms, so residents can check their appearance.

Independence Objectives

1. To enable residents the right to use mechanical lifts within the Home, if they are deemed capable of doing so.

2. To enable a resident their independent use of bathing equipment's if desired.

3. The right for a resident to leave The Home at any time that they choose for particular purpose that they may have in mind, if deemed to be responsible.

4. The right for a resident to be able to clean their own bedrooms and make their own bed or not to do so.

5. To enable residents to handle their own financial affairs when able to do so themselves.

6. The right for a resident to choose independently their own furnishings of their bedroom is they so wish to.

7. The right of independent choice of meals by offering a choice of meals within The Home.

8. The right to be able to have tea-making facilities within ones bedroom.

9. The right to be able to control one's own medication (if deemed responsible).

10. The right that staff will respect and understand a resident's wish for independent needs and preferences within The Home.

11. Staff will deliver care **with** people rather than **for** people.

12. Residents will be able to control their own temperature of their bedroom, lighting and opened windows etc

Choice Objectives

1. The right to choose where they live.
2. The choice to continue to be a smoker.
3. The right to choose to get away from smokers, TV, radio, etc.
4. The right to be able to choose of 2 choices of meals prior to meal times.
5. The right for residents to choose when they are bathed.
6. The right of any resident to choose their own Carer, if for any reason that they are dissatisfied with current Carer/resident relationship.
7. The right for a resident to choose their own General-Practitioner, if there is a preference.
8. The right for any resident to choose their own time for retiring to their bedrooms and the right to decide when they get up.
9. The right for residents to choose their own sitting area within the lounge of The Home.
10. The right for residents to choose their own furnishings for their bedrooms where necessary, and to provide their own furnishings if so desired.
11. The right for residents to eat meals within their own rooms if so desired.

12. The right for residents to choose their clothing to wear for the day.

13. The right for residents to choose their own beverages with The Home.

14. The right for residents to choose their own newspapers and magazines if they so wish to.

15. The right for any resident to have their freedom and views within The Home.

16. Rules will be minimal.

17. The resident to choose their own funeral arrangements.

18. Religious and cultural needs will be encouraged.

Right Objectives

1. The right for residents to decide on the Home they wish to live in.

2. The right to be able to leave the Home when residents require to do so. If at the time deemed responsible.

3. The right to have facilities of the telephone.

4. The right of free speech and views.

5. The rights to choose one's own preferences.

6. Right to make mistakes.

7. Right to vote in general and by elections.

8. The right to have access to their own case files.

9. The right to a Care Plan which is discussed with them.

10. The right to see nurse in private.

Fulfilment Objectives

1. The right for residents to be able to continue their hobbies and interests within The Home, and to be given help and encouragement to fulfil the above mentioned. The right for residents to take holidays away from the Home where deemed able to do so.

2. The right for every resident to be able to share in decision making and offer ideas which may effect and benefit all residents at The Home.

3. The right of freedom to be able to attend Day Centres, Clubs and places of personal interest. The right for residents to be able to attend church regularly and to assist where necessary in order that residents obtain transport etc.

4. The right for residents to be able to return Home at their own times of the day or of the evening.

5. The right to fulfil any ambition that a resident may have and to assist in any way that this ambition can be fulfilled.

6. The right for spiritual and emotional needs to be met.

7. Access to all support services e.g. hairdressing, clergy, library, district nurses, dentist, etc.

PHILOSOPHY OF CARE

To help ensure a quality of life maximising the potential of the individual. Preserve the dignity and self-respect of the individual coupled with the highest quality of care.

To provide support and confidence, with assurance and

To recognise that the right of privacy includes the need to respect the confidential nature of information relating to the client their family and friends.

The right to dignify includes the recognition of, and catering for, an individual's ethnic cultural and religious needs.

To work with the client fostering their independence and respecting their involvement in the planning and the delivery of their care.

To work in a collaborative and co-operative manner with all health professionals. Community and social workers involved in the provision of care and to recognise and respect their contributions within the care team and the structure of the Home.

Conclusion

The Home being a Care Home, some of these can be achieved subject to; Resident/Management Contract, house rules, outcome of Residents Meetings, Policies of the Home, medical and psychiatric community advisers and availability of resources such as finance. Also taking into consideration the resident's physical and mental condition at the time. The home's aim is to achieve these making sure it does not result in dangerous situations to the resident or to other residents and the community.

Senior staff are available to discuss with residents the reason why particular needs cannot be implemented at the time.

Chapter 7

Private and Confidential

APPLICATION FOR EMPLOYMENT FORM

PERSONAL DETAILS:

Name:...............Date of Birth: .

Address: ....

Home No: .... Mobile No:

Age of Dependents: ....

Academic Qualifications: ....

Professional Qualifications: ...

Present Employment: ....

Address and Tel. No.

of present employment: ....

Can your present employer be

contacted for a reference?   YES/NO

Please give two names and addresses for

referees, one of which must be a previous

Employer who wish to give

 references in support of your application

1)   Name: ....

        Address: .....

        In what capacity is this person known to you

2) Name: ....

Address: ....

In what capacity is this person known to you

Do you require full or part-time work?

Are you interested in day/night duty or both?

Are you interested in weekend duty

(permanently/occasionally

Why do you want to do this work? ...

Have you had any experience in caring

for elderly people of differing mental and physical

disability? (yes/no)

If yes, in what capacity ..

Hobbies: ......

Do you drive? (yes/no) If No please

state means of transport:

Employment History for the past 5 years.

Please explain any gaps in employment.

Create a form in the following format

1)Employers name and Address,

2)Position held 3 From 4)to Reason leaving

Health

Have you or do you suspect you have

any physical illness? (yes/no)

If Yes please give details:

Have you ever had or been suspected

of having any mental illness? (yes/no)

If Yes please give name and address of G.P:

May your G.P. be contacted? (yes/no)

Do you have any disabilities? (yes/no)

If Yes please give a brief outline:

Please state any information, such as health issues that you wish us to consider with reference to your application

How would you describe your personality?

Why do you think you are suitable for the job you have applied for? .

Have you any known convictions (yes/no). If yes, please write this/these below.

Known Convictions - In reference to the Rehabilitation of Offenders Act 1974.

"In order to protect the public, the post for which application is being made is exempt from Section 4(2) of the Rehabilitation of Offenders Act 1974 by virtue of the Rehabilitation of Offenders Act 1974 (Exceptions) Order 1975. It is not, therefore, in any way contrary to the Act to reveal any information you may have concerning convictions which would otherwise be considered as 'spent"

Please note that employment is subject to a check from the Criminal Records Bureau, satisfactory, good references (one being from employer) and the decision of the manager at interview. Any acceptance will be conditional on a trial period of at least 6 weeks.

Signed

Date ....For office use only

Comment

Chapter 8

Assessing residents needs

Assessments of prospective clients are carried out prior to admission following our admission criteria and guidelines set by the National Care Standards a second assessment will take place six weeks after admission and thereafter every six months or more frequently if required due to physical and psychological changes.

The manager or her representative will assess all prospective clients, in their own Home or when the person visits the Home.

The methods used are: The Senior Key Worker ascertains individual needs and preferences by speaking to the resident the GP, CPN, Care Manager, Resident's Advocate, Day centre, District Nurse to collate information with the client's consent so the assessment form can then be completed.

A care plan will be discussed and agreed with the client following the outcome of the assessments. All needs identified from the assessment will be added to the care plan by the senior key worker and will state whom is identified to meet specific needs. The Registered Manager will countersign all care plans as to the Homes' commitment to meet these needs.

All needs on the care plan are evaluated every month as per the national care standards by

Chapter 9

ASSISTANT MANAGER – JOB DESCRIPTION

Name:

Role: Assistant Manager in a Residential Home

Title: Assistant Manager

Responsible to: Manager and General Manager

Report to: Manager (In the absence of the Manger to the General Manager or Proprietor)

Minimum Qualifications: DBS Clearance, 2 years' experience in a senior role, to have or to work a towards NVQ level 3 or 4. All mandatory courses completed. Knowledge of client group.

Aims of Post

- To assist the Manager
- To implement approved care policy and legislations in the Home
- To co-ordinate the work of the staff
- To confer with GPs on the treatment of the clients
- To adhere to the aims and objectives of the Home

Key Tasks

1. Organise and maintain an efficient care service throughout the Home day and night in accordance with the National Care Standards 2000 and the Home's Policies and Procedures. Inform the manager of the implementation of such policy and aims/objectives.

2. Maintain contact with the community and clients and their relatives, by acting as the representative of the Home.

3. Maintain a high standard of client care in the Home and channels of communication which ensure that these standards are known and applied.

4. To have knowledge of and implement the National Care Standards, Warren Home life Homes are for living in and the local authority procedures for protection of vulnerable adults.

Functions

1. Instructing and supervising staff as per job description on matters affecting the welfare of the clients. Documentation of this to be kept in staff files. Observing the requirements of the National Care Standards and relevant legislation.

2. Maintaining records of clients.

3. Participating in ensuring clients nutritional needs and supervising the provision of special diets.

4. Ensure routines are followed by staff.

5. Assessing planning, implementing and evaluating the care plans of clients.

6. Participating in drug administration as per medication records.

7. Maintaining equipment and ensuring for the provision for repairs.

8. Instigating emergency repairs and advising the manager of such circumstances.

9. Preparing, receiving and giving reports as required.

10. Ensuring that all staff are familiar with fire prevention, precautions and have received proper instructions e.g. that staff are aware of the action they should take in the event of a fire. Ensure that all fire exits are kept clear and fire notices are permanently and prominently displayed at all times.

11. Participate in in-service training and induction programme for staff.

12. Inform the manager of any special training needs of staff.

13. Use the record of instruction and health and safety at work booklets.

14. Develop skills of other staff members.

15. Attend monthly staff meetings and in the absence of the manager chair the meetings.

16. Organise staff rota as required.

17. Ensure that daily, weekly routines are implemented.

18. Exercising leadership by personal example and maintaining morale of other staff members. Taking possible steps to safeguard the health, welfare and safety, clients, and their relatives in the Home introducing new members of staff to their duties and orientating them to the structure and geography of the Home, control and direct staff by good leadership and example, counselling and supporting staff as required.

19. Monitor and inspect that work is carried out in accordance with agreed Policy.

20. Informing the manager, where appropriate, of accidents or complaints

in the Home and assisting in investigating such incidents in accordance with the Home's Policy.

21. Arranging for safe-keeping of residents property, money and valuables according to the Home's Policy.

22. Co-operate with staff to keep the home clean, tidy and monitor such standards as a matter of routine.

Signed: _____Date

Manager: ____Date

Chapter 10

Bathing

It is advisable not to have a bathing rota in order to avoid institutionalisation and clients' personal tasks working around staff routines. In order to keep a record of baths taken by residents, a bath book may be advisable, or a record should be kept in their care notes.

1. Aim

To promote cleanliness and avoid infection.

2. Method of Bathing

a)   Is a strip wash required?

b)   Does client need a specific kind of bath e.g. medic bath?

3. Assessment and Care Planning

a)   When to have a bath?

b)   Whether assistance is required - is risk assessment necessary?

c)   For certain clients where bathing or tending to personal hygiene is a point of issue; a mutual agreement may be decided upon and therefore agreed days may be an option. This must be stated in the care plan to ensure all staff are aware of this process.

d)   Consent must be obtained first from the resident.

e) Who they want to bathe them? This obviously, being a personal maybe embarrassing procedure. Find out at what stage of bathing they need assistance with, if any?

f) Which bathroom to use?

g) What clothes to be worn afterwards? Does the resident need assistance to choose clothes or can they do this themselves?

h) Do they wish to use their own toiletries, towels, etc?

4. Preparation of Bathroom

a) Is the bathroom warm enough (radiators on, windows closed)?

b) Is there a bath mat in the bath to avoid slipping?

c) Is there a bath thermometer

d) Is there a stool to sit on?

e) Are there sufficient toiletries, towels, etc?

f) Are the curtains closed?

g) Is there a basket for dirty laundry?

If resident wants to be dressed in the bathroom, remember to take clothes to the bathroom, if not take a dressing gown.

5.   Procedure Before and on Bathing Resident

Firstly obtain the resident's consent. If client requires supervision throughout the procedure - they should not be left alone - everything that is needed should be in the bathroom before starting.

a)   Door should be locked

b)   Bath water should be run (some cold water first)

c)   Staff should check that the water temperature is not above 43°C. This is to be tested via a bath thermometer.

d)   Remember help may only be needed to get in and out of the bath. It is not always necessary to stand over someone whilst they are bathing but make sure the call bell is within reach

e)   Staff should not lift residents out of the bath by themselves

f)   Carry out observation of resident's body for any abnormality and report to the person if charge and their key worker.

6.   After Bathing the Resident

a)   Escort resident back to lounge or bedroom if necessary

b) Bath should be washed out thoroughly after use with detergent

c) Bath mat should also be washed (both sides), bacterial spray used, then rinsed and hung up to dry

d) Any fabric bath mats used must only be used once and then put out for washing

e) Soiled clothing, used towels should be taken to the laundry for washing

f) The hoist or any other bathing aid must be thoroughly cleaned

g) Open the window

h) Leave the bathroom clean and tidy for the next person

Chapter 11

Body Temperature

For the body to function optimally it's temperature must be maintained. Normal body temperature ranges between 36°c - 37°c by month. However, in practice body temperature varies amongst individuals, but also in the same person being affected by sleep. Exercise and the time of day – lowest 3am and highest 6 pm. In fertile women, body temperature varies in their menstrual cycle – lowest at menstruation – highest at ovulation.

Temperature taken rectally is higher by approximately 0.3°c and lower in the armpit 0.2°c. When body temperature drops the brain stimulates nerves to cause shivering which generates heart by muscle activity and constricts blood vessels which reduce heat loss conversely when body temperature rises the brain stimulates sweating and widens blood vessels in the skin to increase heat loss.

Symptoms

At times a person may have a high temperature and yet complain that they are feeling cold. Confusion or delirium sometimes occurs, and a very high temperature may cause seizures if left untreated. It is important to keep this person in a warm environment – without piling on lots of clothes, bedding etc. – as doing this the body temperature will rise, as you would be making the body warmer.

Treatment

A high temperature – above 37.5°c usually indicates an infection, flu etc., paracetamol may be given every 4 hours to reduce temperature.

Light clothing to be applied – be careful not be reduce a person's temperature to quickly as the body will not be able to cope and this causes seizures.

A warm room is the best environment with a cool fan on the table really helps.

Most adult's temperature is taken orally by mouth for one minute unless they are confused whereas it should be taken under the arm – for two minutes.

The medical term for a high temperature is paraxial. Therefore, a person who does not have a high temperature is a paraxial.

Chapter 12

FORMAT FOR RESIDENT'S CASE HISTORY

date of birth

place of birth

family: parents - occupation, date of death

        married life

        children – names & ages

        family contacts

        brothers & sisters – names whether they are alive and where they live address

school: name and location

        age started and finished school

        academic qualifications

        professional qualifications

        favoured sports

        friends

        likes and dislikes at school e.g.

teachers,

subjects

employment: age started, place of work

        position

        what the work involved

hours

how long in each job

pay

retirement from work

experiences: most important or unusual experience they will never forget

hobbies: favourite hobbies at work, school, retirement, pets

travel: countries visited or holiday destinations

social life: cinema, theatre, drinking, smoking, gambling. things they've enjoyed doing

personality: introvert, extrovert

illness: diagnosis physical major illness, hospital admissions, operations (what and when), disability

mental - illness resulting, hospital admission

senses - sight, hearing smell, touch taste etc.

why admitted to this home/background to admission

family/friends contacts at present:

Chapter 13

CARE HOME REGULATIONS ABSTRACT; Regulation 37

Of the Care Home Regulation replaced Regulation 14 of the Registered Homes Act. Notification of Death, Illness, Incident or Accident. The local CSCI office must be notified in writing within 24 hours.

Regulation 38 Notice of Absence of the manager for more than 6 weeks.

Regulation 26 Visit and report of Registered Person.

Record of events which must be kept under Schedule 4.

a)   Any accidents

b)   Outbreak of Infectious Diseases

c)   Injury or Illness

d)   Any Fire

e)   Theft or Burglary

f)   Any incidents of violence

Chapter 14

CHARTER OF RIGHTS FOR RESIDENTS

As a resident of our home you should enjoy the following rights :

THE RIGHT; to have your personal dignity respected, irrespective of physical or mental disability

THE RIGHT; to be treated as an individual in your own right

THE RIGHT; to personal independence, personal choice and personal responsibility for actions

THE RIGHT to undertake for yourself those daily living tasks which you are able to do

THE RIGHT to personal privacy for yourself, your belongings and your affairs

THE RIGHT to have your cultural, religious, sexual and emotional needs accepted and respected

THE RIGHT to the same access to facilities and services in the community as any other citizen

THE RIGHT to maintain and develop social contacts and interests

THE RIGHT to manage your own financial and private affairs

THE RIGHT to control your own medication and to make decisions about your medical treatment in conjunction with your doctor

THE RIGHT to receive care appropriate to your needs from suitably trained or experienced workers

THE RIGHT to participate as fully as possible in the formulation of your own individual care plans before and during your stay

THE RIGHT to have, and to participate in, regular reviews of your individual circumstances, and to have a friend or adviser present if you so wish

THE RIGHT to expect management and staff to accept where appropriate the risks associated with encouragement of personal independence

THE RIGHT to be fully informed about the services provided by the home and of any decisions made by the homes staff that may affect your personal well-being

THE RIGHT to take part in making decisions about daily living arrangements in the home, and to be consulted about any proposed changes

THE RIGHT to be represented by an advocate, if you so wish, or if you are unable to make personal representation through mental incapacity

THE RIGHT to access to your personal files in line with the homes procedure

THE RIGHT of access to a formal complaints procedure and to be represented by a friend or adviser as you so wish

You must also bear in mind the rights of the staff and the team of carers e.g. doctors, nurses, social workers, inspectors etc.

YOUR RESPONSIBILITIES

No one has complete freedom to do as they please - we all have to take account of the needs of others

RISK OF HAVING RIGHT

It is important to realise that rights and independence brings with it an element of risk - some degree of risk is a normal part of life. Avoidance of all risks leads to an unhealthy way of life.

RESTRICTIONS

For therapeutic reasons those individuals with severe disabilities or mental health problems, may not be able to exercise their rights in full. The management at the home will make all efforts not to take away your rights unnecessarily - and any restriction will be strictly limited and reviewed regularly

If for any reason you feel you are unnecessarily being denied your rights:

1) Talk to the manager first
   if this is unsuccessful
2) Talk or write to the national care standards commission
3) Follow the complaint procedure

Chapter 15

Guidelines to staff about residents' rights within the community or residential home

Everybody must respect the right of another within the guidelines of the home's policies. This applies to staff, residents, inspectors, visitors, next of kin etc.

A right is a privilege that is or should have been delivered without question

A right is the maintenance of all entitlements associated with citizenship

Residents have the right to :

Express their feelings.

Express their opinions and values.

To say yes or no for themselves.

Change their minds.

To make mistakes.

To deal with others without being dependent on them for approval.

To decline responsibility for other people's problems.

To ask for what they want.

To use all of the communal areas in the home.

to refuse staff access to in their bedrooms.

to act within the law or the contract of the home.

to choose, be independent, be respected.

to privacy.

to refuse treatment .

to say i don't understand and ask for more information.

to be told the truth (in some cases e.g. therapeutic reasons or by clinical judgement, information may be withheld from residents).

RESIDENT'S RIGHT TO REFUSE TREATMENT

All adult/ elderly mentally competent persons have the right to refuse treatment even if the personal consequences may be severe.

N.B. Staff or GP should ensure that the resident is fully aware of the consequences of refusal and if possible, arrange help or counselling with residents' consent. They have the right to know what the staff and doctor discuss, and consent should be given prior to discussion.

N.B. Consequences of denial of resident's rights includes criminal liabilities for assault, battery, imprisonment.

Right of access to Personal Files Act 1987 - An individual may require the record to be amended if incorrect.

N.B. Provision is made in the act for disclosure to be refused or be restricted on the basis of a prejudice to the proper carrying out of social work.

Right of Access to Medical Reports Act 1988 - If any organisation such as insurance, court, require a resident's medical report or care plan the resident must give his consent first. When the report is prepared, the resident must be given 21 days to exercise his/her right to correct any errors or change his/her mind.

N.B. Residents access to medical files may be refused or restricted on therapeutic grounds or where identity of another person would be disclosed.

Access to Health Records Act 1990 - With effect from November 1991, the resident has the right to have access to manual health records concerning him/her kept after that date and to earlier records to the extent that this is necessary to make the later records intelligible. A resident has the right for the records to be amended. Access may be restricted where the information is deemed to be harmful

The staff have a duty to explain the records to the extent that the resident can understand what is written.

In the case of complaint, internal grievance procedure must be exhausted before the matter can be taken to court.

In summary - Although the residents have rights to various health and care records, these can be withheld or restricted on the grounds that disclosure would be likely to cause serious harm to the physical or mental health of the resident or would be likely to disclose confidential information as to the identity of another resident.

Residents in the Residential Home have many other unwritten rights which staff must allow.

Staff care for residents;

1.   Residents should not be subject to inhuman or degrading treatment.

2.   Encourage freedom of conscience, thought and religion.

3.   Encourage freedom of expression, right to complain.

4.   Respect private life, confidentiality of personal affairs and space.

5.Safeguard individual rights without discriminating on any grounds whether gender, age, race, colour, language, religion or other status or political or other opinion

6.The management is to monitor the homes performance in safeguarding residents' rights.

7.Provision of a stimulating environment, care, control, choice.

8.Promote emotional and physical well-being e.g. worthiness, responsibility,

9.   Pursuit of intellectual, religious and cultural matters

Chapter 16

CODE OF CONDUCT FOR RESIDENTS

a) Residents must not enter other residents' rooms without the occupant's permission.

b) Clients are asked to treat other residents, staff and visitors as they would like to be treated.

c) Theft

The home reserves the right to use whatever means are necessary including legal action to recover any item belonging to the home which is stolen by the resident.

d) Persistent unsociable behaviour will not be tolerated if this is distressing to other residents and staff.

e) Willful damage will be charged for.

The Home reserves the right to use whatever means are necessary including legal action to recover any item belonging to the Home which is stolen by the resident. If clients do not adhere to the Home's Code of Conduct, they may be requested to find an alternative establishment.

Chapter 17

CODE OF CONDUCT FOR STAFF

Staff must always act in a professional manner whilst on duty or when representing the Home. They must use appropriate language and not swear. Residents must not ever be called by nicknames.

Alcohol or illegal substances must not be used whilst on duty.

Smoking is permitted but only during breaks and in designated area. Effective communication must be used. Messages must be recorded in the diary and not on pieces of paper. These must be passed onto the relevant person or during handover. All notes concerning residents are to be recorded in relevant places.

All clients, other staff, visitors to the home must be treated in an anti-discriminating way.

Policy – Abide by the policy of the Home and the instructions therein at all times.

Confidentiality – Information pertaining to the Residents/Staff and Proprietor should not be disclosed to any enquirer or be given to anybody within or outside the Home without the Manager's/Proprietor's written and signed permission – refer to Policy of the Home.

– Staff should present themselves for duty clean and tidy. Staff must read and adhere to the detailed dress code.

Long hair should be tied back. Suitable, comfortable footwear must be worn (no high heels, boots or opened toes shoes without backings). Rings with sharp surfaces, nail varnish, long nails are not allowed; any damage inflicted upon residents will be viewed as a serious matter.

Punctuality – Must be on time for work. Must be prepared to stay until other staff have taken over before going off duty.

Chapter 18

COMMUNITY CARE FORM

It is important to record the following form residents care notes – Please include *names* and *titles.*

1. Visits and phone calls to and from GP's
2. Residents attending GP visits to his Surgery
3. Visits and phone calls to and from psychiatrist
4. Residents who go out to see psychiatrist – where they go to i.e. Purley
5. Recourse Centre etc.
6. Visits from Chiropodists
7. Visits from Opticians
8. Visits from Dentist
9. Visits from Incontinence Advisor
10. Any Admissions or discharges to Hospital
11. Hospital Appointments
12. Reviews – In House – Reviewing Officers – Care Managers

It is important to keep these records up to date so that staff can see at a glance when e.g. "Joe Blogs" last saw his psychiatrist, or when he had his last review.

Chapter 19

COMPLAINT / COMMENTS AND SUGGESTIONS
PROCEDURE

While we trust that all our service users will be satisfied with the quality of the care they receive. However there may be occasions when a resident or their relative may wish to raise a concern, or make a formal complaint.

We want you to know that you should always feel free to raise your concerns. It is hoped that a discussion with the manager will resolve the issue. Our complaints procedure is as follows:

We appreciate and welcome your comments, suggestions and complaints so we can improve our services. Any person who makes a complaint will not be discriminated or prejudiced against. The person must make their comments or complaints verbally or in writing in English (or in any language which can then be translated for the record) as soon as possible after the event to the

Manager. If unable to write, ask someone to help you.

The Manager or their representative will acknowledge the comments within 14 days of receipt. If the person is not happy with the initial response, he/she must put this in writing to the proprietor within seven days of receipt.

On receipt of the appeal the proprietor or his representative will endeavor to carry out an investigation and reply within 28 days. If for any reason this may take longer than anticipated the complainant will be notified and the reason given for the delay.

If the person is not happy with the internal investigation (proprietor's reply) he/she must inform the proprietor in writing and if they decide to continue the complaint this must be done within 14 days. After that the home will consider the matter closed.

Having said the above, if the complaint cannot be locally resolved or if the complainant is dissatisfied with the proprietor's decision they also have the right to make their complaint to the National Care Standards Commission . The current name and address and telephone of the National Care Standards Commission: (insert Address and tel.)

At any stage of the complaint, the complainant may contact the Commission for Social Care Inspection direct on the following address and telephone number:

Commission for Social Care Inspection

(address and tele)

If not happy with the Inspectors decision you may approach the Citizens Advice Bureau, current address:

Citizens Advice Bureau

(address and tele)

or   Local Ombudsman

21 Queen Anne's Gate

London

SW1H 9BU

You can also complain to your placement authority through your care manager.

In order to establish and maintain a good relationship with our residents and visitors who may have a complaint, after investigations the proprietor has in place a discretionary reparation policy, if the complaint is upheld.

The Home has suggestion and comments forms, which are located by the resident's noticeboard. These can be completed and placed in the "comments/suggestions box" which is opened and actioned by the manager weekly.

Evaluations of the Care Plan are carried out on a monthly basis. Formal reviews are held 6 monthly to assess whether there are changes in the service user's condition making significant amendments to the Care Plan imperative in the interests of the resident.

Chapter 20

COMPLAINTS FORM

Name of Complainant:

Name of Service User/Staff (if applicable):

And Name and address of

complainant if applicable

Date Complaint received: Date Resolved:

Telephone:

Yes/No

Letter:

Yes/No

Fax:

Yes/No

Date acknowledgement letter sent:

(Within14 days of receipt)

Investigation carried by:

Action Take as a result of complainant

Investigation transcript on file Yes/No

Letter sent to complainant covering

investigation outcome and action

taken where appropriate Yes/No

Standard paragraph added to letter:

If your compliant is still not dealt with
to your satisfaction, then a
complaint about the management
of the Home can be made, in writing to

Date sent to Proprietor:

Date investigation commence:

Date of completion of investigation:

Date letter sent to complainant

Re: Outcome of complain

Meeting to discuss findings if appropriate:

Copy of all documentation on file

Signature of investigators of compliant

Signature and designation   Date:

Signature of the Proprietor:

Name of complainant:

(Please Print)

Letter sent to complainant by recorded
 delivery where applicable

Signature   Date:

Proprietor or General Manager (if applicable)

Chapter 21

CONFIDENTIALITY AND ACCESS TO FILES

AS PER THE DATA PROTECTION ACT

Information pertaining to the residents/staff and proprietor should not be disclosed to any enquirer or to be given to anybody within or outside the home without the manager's/proprietor's consent (written signed permission).

Known inspectors from CSCI (upon proven identification) are allowed to see documents as per The National Care Standards and regulations.

Please note it is a very serious offence to disclose confidential information to unauthorised personnel, i.e., your relatives, members of the public or to other staff without the consent of the resident (unless non-disclosure of the information would result in placing the resident or other people in any danger -permission to disclose information should be sought in the first instance).

Please read the Data Protection Act.

Residents are allowed to see their own records. If residents request access to their files they can arrange an appointment to view these with the Manager. Certain restrictions may apply to individual residents, these instances will be referred to the client's GP or Care Manager.

Access To Files (Residents and Staff);

There are normally two types of file for each person:-

a) an open file *and* b) a closed file

Open File

contains information which a person is allowed access to and this should be given to him/her by either the employer (in the case of staff) or by the manager (in the case of residents). The person is allowed to ask questions and has the right to receive honest answers to any query in the file. The file should not be removed from the premises and there will be someone in the room to ensure that the staff or the resident do not remove anything from the file.

Closed File

A 'closed file' contains documents which the person (staff or resident) is not entitled to see.

In the case of a resident the file may contain doctor's recommendations or information received from relatives or friends who have specifically requested that the information should not be disclosed to the resident e.g., a terminal illness is diagnosed but the doctor may feel that by informing that particular resident it may result in a more serious outcome like an attempt at suicide. Another example is a team of doctors and the next of kin of the resident may agree that the resident should not receive resuscitation, which should under no circumstances be disclosed to the resident. If a client requests such information the resident will be referred to his/her medical practitioner.

Any information produced by a third party can only be shown to the resident when the permission of the originator has been received in writing.

In the case of staff all references received in support of the person's employment application. Any information received from anyone marked 'private and confidential'.

Clients have the right to choose where they see their visitors, e.g. family, friends, doctors, care managers. A private area e.g. bedroom can be used. Those who share a bedroom may be offered an alternative private area. Staff must not invade client's privacy and respect their wishes to be left alone with their visitors. Clients must also be encouraged to take telephone calls in private.

CONFIRMATION OF RECEIPT:

Name:

Date:

*Delete as applicable

I have *received/do not require a copy of the Service Users Guide and Statement of Purpose

Signature:

Name: (print please)

Chapter 22

CONTRACT OF EMPLOYMENT

The management hereby offers full/part-time employment to: _____

This will become void if it comes to the notice of management that the applicant has given false information or failed to give any information in writing which in his/her opinion would have prevented the applicant being offered the post.

Mr/Mrs/Ms/Miss _____

In the capacity of _____

This employment commences on _____ (am/pm)

If full-time state hours _____If part-time state minimum hours _____

REMUNERATION

At the rate of £ _____ per hour to be paid monthly by cheque/cash.

Excluding/Including Income Tax and National Insurance contributions.

A wages review will take place annually.

criminal records bureau/ DBS

All posts are subject to a check made by the Criminal Records Bureau which is to be paid by the employee.

ANNUAL LEAVE

As per present Government guidelines.

Unpaid leave can be taken within the year by arrangement with the Proprietor/Manager.

MATERNITY LEAVE

As per Government present guidelines.

SICK PAY

If Tax/National Insurance is deducted then SSP entitlement is automatically paid on the production of Self Certification or a Medical Certificate. If employment period is less than 6 months the claimant should apply to the DSS for SSP. Employee may be requested to apply to DSS for SSP even if employment is more than 6 months.

Persistent intermittent sickness on self-certificate will require verification from the GP of good health at the person's own expense and medical clearance must be obtained before reinstatement of employment. If a period of sickness exceeds one week a medical certificate will be required.

Some types of sickness leave which are lengthy (operations, etc.) will require a review of the person's job description as well as a certificate of good health and capacity to do the job will be required before reinstatement of employment. Other options of employment within the Home may be applicable.

REFERENCES

Staff may be employed, and their contractual rights respected pending two written references, received before employment. One reference being from a previous employer and one-character reference. According to the national minimum standards for Care Homes Standard 29.1. However if the manager after receiving satisfactory verbal reference may employ you subject to the two references received within one month. If not the management reserves the right to withdraw employment.

All staff employed will have a trial period of 4 to six weeks for both their benefit and the Home's. After which, when references are received or if already received, full contractual employment will be offered or termination decided by one or both parties. The trial period may be shortened or extended at the discretion of the management. During or after this period the management reserves the right to terminate employment giving 24 hours' notice.

DOCUMENTS

The employee must show originals of the following documents before offer of employment, copies will be retained by the Home.

1) Passport (and work permit if applicable or proof to work in the UK)

2) Evidence of address

3) A completed Health Questionnaire

4) Birth Certificate (if an original birth certificate is not available, evidence that a copy has been applied for)

5) A passport size photograph

Failure to produce these documents will result in the employee not being offered a contract.

MATERNITY PAY

May be paid after one year's continual service at SMB rate. If less than one year the claimant should apply to the DSS.

TERMINATION

Employment may be terminated by one month's notice on either side.

The Proprietor reserves the right to terminate employment without giving full notice for misconduct or behaviour not compatible with the aims of the establishment.

The Home operates an instant dismissal policy for serious misconduct, breach of confidentiality or behaviour not compatible with the aims of the establishment, which does not require a verbal or written warning.

ROUTINE

The Proprietor and Manager's instructions are to be carried out without hindrance at all times in respect of routine, policy, including any changes therein, aims and objectives of the Home as per job description. (In the absence of the Manager, the Proprietor, the General Manager or the Deputy Manager may act for the Manager.)

The Manager must be prepared to provide reasonable physical, environmental and psychological care to the Residents.

VALUABLES

The Home accepts no responsibility for money, valuables and possessions brought into the Home by staff, being stolen or damaged, whilst staff is on duty. Such as items brought into the Home are entirely at the person's own risk.

STAFF / TEAM MEETINGS

Staff must be prepared to attend meetings held by the Home. Failure to attend such meetings will result in the management taking disciplinary action.

CODE OF CONDUCT

Staff must act always in a professional manner whilst on duty or when representing the home. They must use appropriate language and not swear. Residents must not ever be called by Nick names.

Alcohol or illegal substances must not be used whilst on duty.

Smoking is permitted but only during breaks and in designated area. Effective communication must be used. Messages must be recorded in the diary and not on piece on paper. These must be passed onto the relevant person or during handover. All notes concerning residents are to be recorded in relevant places.

All clients, other staff, visitors to the home must be treated in an anti-discriminating way.

Policy - Abide by the policy of the Home and the instructions therein at all times.

Confidentiality - Information pertaining to the Residents/ Staff and Proprietor should not be disclosed to any enquirer or be given to anybody within or outside the Home without the Manager's

/Proprietor's consent written signed permission - refer to Policy of the Home.

Appearance & Presentation - Staff should present themselves for duty clean and tidy. Female staff must not wear jeans during day duty. No shorts or miniskirts. Female night staff may wear trousers.

Long hair should be tied back. Suitable, comfortable footwear must be worn (no high heels, boots or opened toed shoes without backings). Rings with sharp surfaces, nail varnish, long nails are not allowed; any damage inflicted upon residents will be viewed as a serious matter.

Punctuality - Must be on time for work. Must be prepared to stay until other staff have taken over before going of duty.

Chapter 23

DISCIPLINARY CODE AND GRIEVANCE PROCEDURE

DISCIPLINARY CODE

A   PURPOSE AND SCOPE

Whilst it is sometimes necessary to discipline and in extreme cases dismiss an employee the main purpose of the disciplinary procedure is to help and encourage all employees to achieve and maintain standards of conduct attendance and job performance. The aim is to ensure consistent and fair treatment for all.

B   GENERAL PRINCIPLES

1   This Code shall cover all employees with the exception of new employees working on a probationary period.

2   All employees when permanently engaged will be given a copy of their Terms and Conditions of Employment and of this procedure and it is their duty to ensure that these are fully understood.

3   No disciplinary action will be taken against an employee until the case has been fully investigated.

4   At every stage in the procedure the employee will be advised of the nature of the complaint against him or her and will be

given the opportunity to state his or her case before any decision is made.

5   At all stages the employee will have the right to be accompanied by a shop steward employee representative or work colleague during the disciplinary interview.

6   No employee will be dismissed for a first breach of discipline except in the case of gross misconduct when the penalty will be dismissal without notice or payment in lieu of notice.

7   An employee will have the right to appeal against any disciplinary penalty imposed.

8   The procedure may be implemented at any stage if the employee's alleged misconduct warrants such action.

9   Since dismissal is the ultimate sanction it is anticipated that its use will be confined to rare cases.   There will be no dismissal without the specific authority of the Managing Director.

C   PROCEDURE

Before the implementation of the formal procedure informal discussions and counselling will take place to establish whether the problem is in fact a disciplinary one and may not be dealt with by other means.

Where initial discussions establish that the matter is more serious or may involve repeated minor errors the following procedure will be used and at every stage hereafter the Manager will be consulted before any decision is taken to ensure that the procedure has been complied with.

Any warning whether written or oral will remain valid for a period of 12 months. In the event that the employee's performance is satisfactory throughout that period the warning and any previous warnings shall upon expiry of the period be disregarded for disciplinary purposes.

Stage 1   Oral Warning

If conduct or performance does not meet acceptable standards the Manager will interview the employee and if appropriate give the employee a formal oral warning. He or she will be advised of the reason for the warning that it is the first stage of the disciplinary procedure and of his or her right of appeal. A brief note of the oral warning will be kept.

Stage 2   First Written Warning

In the event of the conduct complained of not being rectified or in the event of a further offence there will be a further discussion between the Manager and the Proprietor, and the Manager will give a written warning specifying the conduct complained of and a time limit for improvement. It will warn that action under stage 3 will be considered if there is no satisfactory improvement and will advise of the right of appeal. The warning will be confirmed in writing and a copy sent to the Managing Director.

Stage 3   Final Warning

In the event of the conduct complained of still not being rectified or in the event of further misconduct there will be a further meeting between the Manager and the employee at which a further written warning will be given to the employee specifying:-

(a)   A clear statement of that conduct

(b)   A plan and time limit for improvement

(c)   That disciplinary action involving redeployment demotion or Dismissal (as the case may be) could result if there is not Improvement within the specified time limit or if there is a Recurrence of the misconduct.

When the action has been taken a copy of the warning given to the employee together with any relevant information is placed in the employee's record.   The employee should acknowledge receipt of this warning in writing.

Stage 4   Redeployment   Demotions   or Dismissal

Disciplinary Interview

In the event of the conduct complained of not being rectified or in the event of gross misconduct the Manager shall carry out a full investigation into the relevant facts and a disciplinary interview shall be held at which the employee the Manager and the General Manager shall be present.

An employee may be suspended on full pay pending the investigation and the disciplinary interview.

The employee shall be given 2 clear days' notice in writing of the disciplinary interview and such notice shall state that disciplinary action including dismissal may be taken against the employee as a result of the interview.

The interview shall be conducted by the Manager who shall inform the employee of the details of the conduct being complained of and the results of his investigation. The employee shall then be given an opportunity of explanation.

The Manager and the General Manager shall then decide whether further investigation is required and if it is shall adjourn the interview and reconvene when the investigation is completed.

Following the interview the Manager and General Manager shall decide what disciplinary action if any is appropriate and shall notify the employee in writing of their decision the reasons and the employee's right of appeal. If dismissal is deemed appropriate the General Manager shall obtain the specific authority of the Managing Director.

Types of Disciplinary Action;

(a)   Suspension

Suspension from work can be without pay and for a period of between 2 and 5 days depending on the circumstances. If an employee is absent due to sickness on the days when suspension falls due the suspension will be served after his/her return.

(b)   Redeployment Demotion and Down Grading

In certain circumstances where misconduct amounts to a breach of responsibility or failure to reach normally accepted standards the Company may demote transfer redeploy or otherwise down-grade an employee as an alternative to suspension or dismissal.

(c)   Dismissal;

If conduct or performance is still unsatisfactory and the employee still fails to reach the prescribed standards dismissal will normally result. There will be no dismissal without the specific authority of the Managing Director.

Gross Misconduct

Some offences may be judged as gross misconduct in which case dismissal without previous warnings will normally result. The following are examples of gross misconduct:-

(a)   Theft fraud deliberate falsification of records

(b)   Fighting assault on another person

(c)   Deliberate damage to company property

(d)   Serious incapability through alcohol or being under the influence of illegal drugs

(e)   Serious negligence which causes unacceptable loss damage or injury

(f)   Serious act of insubordination

When an allegation of gross misconduct is raised the employee shall be suspended on full pay and told when to attend a disciplinary interview. The matter will then be dealt with as specified in Stage 4 above.

If on completion of the investigation and the full disciplinary procedure the Company is satisfied that the employee is guilty of gross misconduct the result will normally be summary dismissal without notice or payment in lieu of notice.

D   APPEALS AGAINST THE DISCIPLINARY ACTION

1   If an employee wishes to appeal against disciplinary action other than dismissal

he/she has the right of appeal to the General Manager.

2   Appeal should always be made by notice in writing given to the General Manager and is to be made within 5 working days of receipt of notification of the disciplinary action or the issue of warning.

3   Further appeal may be made to the Managing Director upon notice in writing given to the Managing Director and is to be made within 5 working days of the decision being appealed against.

4   Appeal against dismissal should be made to the Managing Director in writing within 5 working days of dismissal. If the appeal is upheld the employee will be reinstated to his or her former post.

5   The decision of the Managing Director is final.

E   GRIEVANCE PROCEDURE

1   Initial Action

The employee should raise the matter orally or in writing with the Manager. The Manager will either take a decision on the matter or if he thinks it appropriate refer it to the General Manager. The decision will be given to the employee within 2 days the

Manager shall make a short report for the information of the Managing Director.

2 Appeal

If the employee wishes to appeal against a decision of the Manager he/she has the right of appeal to the General Manager and then a further right of appeal to the Managing Director.

3 Employee Representative

An employee may be accompanied at any of the interviews or appeals if he/she so wishes by a shop steward employee representative or work colleague.

4 Mode of Appeal

(a) Appeal should always be made by notice in writing to the General

Manager or Managing Director as appropriate within 5 working

days of a decision being appealed against.

(b) The decision of the Managing Director is final.

TRAINING

All staff should ensure they are aware of the following with 7 days of employment:

a)   The Health and Safety at Work Act.

b)   Fire Precaution, Prevention and Emergency Procedure in the event of fire.

c)   The record of instruction and Skills for Care induction as prepared by the management.

d)   Employees must be willing to attend courses which the CSCI and management indicate is necessary to care for our clientele.

COMPLAINTS

The person must put his or her grievance or complaint in writing (in English) to the Proprietor within 3 days of the event. The Proprietor and her representative will acknowledge with 3 days and reply within 14 days of receipt. If there is any delay you will be given a reason verbally or in writing e.g. delay in investigation. If the person is still not happy with the initial response he/she must put this is writing to the proprietor within 3 days of receipt.

The proprietor or his representative will endeavour to carry out an investigation and reply within 28 days of given the person a reason.

If the person is not happy with the internal investigation (proprietor's reply) he/she must inform the proprietor in writing and if they decide to continue the complaint proceeding this must be done within 14 days. After that the home will consider the matter closed.

Having said the above, the individual has the right to make their complaint to the Inspection Unit or see changes to Complaints and Procedure documen

If still not happy with the Inspectors decision you may approach the Citizens Advice Bureau, current address

or   Local Ombudsman

Lastly we wish to make it clear that any person that makes a complaint will not be discriminated or prejudiced against.

PERSONAL DETAILS

National Insurance Number

P45 Produced   (Date

Not Produced   (Date)

Date of Birth

Address

Telephone

Next of Kin

Address

Telephone   Work

I, the undersigned confirm that I have read the job description attached and will implement it and the contents of this contract. I undertake to read and implement the Homes Policies within one month of my employment as listed within the Induction Pack and all other Home Policies within three months.

Signature

Manager's Signature

Proprietor's Signature

Date:

Chapter 24

DYING, DEATH AND BEREAVEMENT PROCEDURE

CARE OF THE DYING

OBJECTIVE

1. Staff should respect persons who are terminally ill to die in peace and dignity, as per the NHS End of Life Care Programme. (EOLC) to ensure good practice is being maintained.

2. Ensure residents given appropriate privacy in the terminal stage of their lives.

3. Staff must be satisfied that they are all fully aware of how they should support dying residents, their fellow residents and relatives, and that they are able to practice what they know

4. That relatives and friends are involved in the care of the dying resident, if this is their wish.

5. Ensure all medical advice and care is freely available, and that a detailed care plan is in place, which is being implemented and regularly reviewed.

ADVICE

1. Staff should ensure that dying residents are relieved of distress and pain.

2. In the terminal stage of life, while they are still able to drink, residents should be given enough fluid to allay thirst.

3. Relatives should be afforded every opportunity to be with the resident and to help with care, if that is a mutual agreement.

4. The period of terminal care is cause for great sensitivity to the mental, physical, social and spiritual needs of the dying resident and for an awareness of the strain that the situation places on the family.

5. The resident and his/her family can be given practical help and emotional support by members of the medical team and by helpers from the local authority such as district nurses and by the management of the home who may be involved at some stage.

6. There must be a need for positive approach both to pain and the residents' attitudes to pain. Treatment is composed of listening, attention to detail and skill in handling drugs. Choice of drugs is the responsibility of the medical staff officer.

PROCEDURE FOR DEATH

DEFINITION OF DEATH

When the heartbeat and the respiration (breathing) stops irreversibly.

SIGNS

No pulse, no respiration, loss of physical and mental function, no reaction to painful stimuli, cyanosis (blue coloring) around the extremities-fingers, toes, face etc. Pupils dilate, the skin becomes cold and clammy when dead for a while.

PROCEDURE

If staff see a resident taking a last breath or the heart and respiration stopped within 3 minutes, the procedure for resuscitation must be applied. (Unless the resident or his or her advocator and G.P. have stated otherwise) and these wishes have been documented and witnessed.

If the signs of death as stated above are prominent and resuscitation fails:-

1.   Inform the G.P. that the resident APPEARS TO BE DEAD - give your reasons why you

suspect this e.g. no pulse, no respiration. Do not call an ambulance as only a GP/Doctor can certify a death.

2.   After the G.P. has confirmed the death obtain.

3.   Check the resident's admission form for specific wishes e.g. choice of undertaker.

4.   Inform the next of kin who will give instructions.

Refer to the home policy under "What to do after a bereavement on different religions"

The undertaker should then be informed if next of kin have instructed this.

1.   When the undertaker arrives, they should be taken to the resident's room to collect the body. (Make sure any jeweler has been removed and recorded in the Property/Valuables Book for safe keeping). Jeweler must be handed over during the Handover Procedure until a member of the management can be put the item into the safe. It will, in turn, be given to the next of kin or person specified previously by the deceased.

2.   If visitors are present before the body is taken, they can be taken to a quiet private area and support and advice should be offered at this stressful time. Refer to home

policy "What to do after bereavement in all religions".

3. Record in register of resident's book and care notes

4. Record on admission form details of death.

5. Staff to also notify care manager, day centers or any outside activities that the residents are involved in. If applicable, night staff should pass on during handover whom they wish to be notified.

6. All medication belonging to the deceased must be kept for at least seven days before being returned to the pharmacy, this is because if there is to be a Coroner's Investigation they may be needed for examination.

What to do after a bereavement

Different religions have unique ways of handling a dead person. This must be respected.

Newly bereaved relatives can be thrown into confusion when faced with practical arrangements at a time when they have to come to terms with their grief.

The carer or nurse may offer support and advice at this stressful time.

What to do in all religion

The nurse or carer can facilitate the grief reaction by giving permission to grieve whether at one's own death or the death of a loved one:

1   by encouraging overt signs of grief

2   by not being afraid to grieve with the person(s) concerned by showing concern and care

3   by being present although knowing there is nothing to give other than being there ready to be used as adviser consoler and "whipping boy" for others anger and resentment

4   by giving "permission" to the family to withdraw temporarily

To be able to achieve this degree of involvement the carer needs:

1   Empathy to stand in the shoes and look out through the eye socket (Greek definition)

2   Courage to accept involvement not to shy away and not to become embarrassed,

3   Stamina to be continually open and aware of the pain to others

4 Understanding good team and support from colleagues

The demands made on the carer, by grieving people, are physical, mental, emotional, spiritual and need to be recognised and understood. The carers experiences may led them to use protective mechanisms an almost unconscious withdrawal for self-protection, e.g. busy efficiency that can shut out deep thought and feeling; a refusal to accept anything other than superficial relationships guards against hurt to self.

DEATH AT HOME OR IN HOSPITAL - Refer to Client's Specific Death Wishes

When death occurs expectedly and peacefully at home, the deceased's doctor should be informed straightaway. If cremation is planned the GP and a second doctor must view the body. Usually the doctor who attended the deceased issues a medical certificate of cause of death which is taken to the registrar so the death can be registered. If a person has not seen a doctor within 48 hours and the death is unexpected, the case will be referred to the coroner.

The funeral director should be contacted urgently especially if the body is to be laid out and will need to know if the body is to stay at home or be removed to the chapel of rest. If the bereaved do not want the body embalmed the funeral director must be told as some try to insist on doing this. It is only usual practice to embalm if the body is going to be viewed before the funeral. If the deceased is to be laid out and is wearing clothes and jewellery the funeral director should be instructed what to do with them and how the body is to be dressed.

The medical certificate of cause of death is usually completed by a hospital doctor if one has had the opportunity to assess the cause but otherwise the deceased own doctor is asked to issue the certificate. Once the certificate has been issued the body can be released to the family who can contact a funeral director to collect the body. An executor or a relative sign the authorisation.

If cremation is intended the hospital should be informed. They will then complete the necessary forms for a fee which is normally paid by the funeral director and added to the funeral bill.

REGISTERING A DEATH

The informant, who is to register the death, may be a relative with sufficient information for the registrar, any person present at death or the person arranging the funeral.

Death must be registered within five days at the office of the registrar of Births, Marriages and Deaths for the sub-district where death occurred or where the body was found.

The informant makes an appointment and visits the registrar during office hours taking with them notice given by the doctors. The medical certificate of cause of death should be taken unless the registrar has got this directly from the doctor.

The registrar will need to know the deceased's full name, maiden name (if applicable) sex, date and place of birth, last home address, last full-time occupation and marital status. If the deceased was a married woman or widow her husband's name and job should be given, while the names and occupations of parents is given if in the case of a child under 16.

After the formalities of registering, the registrar issues a certificate of death.

CREMATION

Ashes are usually ready to collect two days later. The crematorium issues a certificate which relatives give to church or cemetery authorities if they intend to scatter or bury the ashes. Some crematoriums have cloister niches or gardens of remembrance for the disposal of ashes, and the cost of these can be checked through the funeral director.

BURIAL

The funeral director will make the necessary arrangements for burial and will need to know the proposed venue; churchyard (or cemetery), private or local authority cemetery, or one other religion.

CHRISTIAN

Anyone has the right to be buried in a churchyard or church cemetery if they died in the parish had their permanent address in the parish or if relatives are buried there (space permitting). Otherwise the funeral director applies to incumbent and parochial church council.

If relatives wish to apply for a "faculty" for the sole use of a plot the funeral director will apply to the diocesan registrar which takes around six weeks. Relatives could apply for a faculty on a grave plot allocated by the incumbent to be used for future burials.

If a churchyard or church cemetery burial is not possible the funeral director may be able to arrange burial in a local cemetery with a plot of consecrated ground. He or she will outline the fees involved and pay them on the relatives behalf. Plots are also sometimes allocated for other denominations and most cemeteries allow religious services of any denomination, but relatives should check details and fees with the funeral director. The next of kin or executor may have to sign an application form for burial in a local authority cemetery. After burial a copy of the entry in the burial register will be issued showing who owns the plot and any previous burials that have taken place on it. The cost of a grave depends on the size and type.

The funeral cortege usually begins from home or the funeral parlour depending on where the body is. Alternatively the body may be taken to the church or cemetery and mourners may gather there.

If the service is in the church bearers take the coffin from the hearse into church and then after the service to the grave site. Should there be no service the coffin is taken directly to the burial site.

The words of committal are said as the coffin is lowered.

Any arrangements for a memorial or headstone are made with the monumental mason. As with all aspects of arranging a funeral it is wise to get detailed estimates of all costs involved before going ahead.

JUDAISM

CARE OF THE DYING

A dying Jew may wish to hear or recite special Psalms, particularly Psalms 23 (The Lord is my Shepherd) and the special prayer (The Shema) and may appreciate being able to hold the page on which it is written.

POST-MORTEM AND ORGAN TRANSPLANTS

The preservation of life is an important guiding principle in Judaism. Therefore although mutilation of a corpse is not permitted there is no objection in principle to organ transplants provided that no organ is removed until death is definitely established.

PROCEDURE AT DEATH

The body should be handled as little as possible by others and burial ideally should take place as soon as practicable preferably within 24 hours of death, and will be delayed only for the Sabbath. (The Sabbath commences before nightfall on Friday and ends on the first sighting of three stars on Saturday evening, hence begins and ends at different times over the year.) Delay for any other cause will cause great distress to the relatives. If death occurs after commencement of the Sabbath, strictly speaking the body should not be moved until after the Sabbath is concluded.

In normal circumstances, where a death certificate will be issued by the attending doctor the eyes should be closed at or soon after death. if practicable this will be performed by one of the children of the deceased. The body should be covered and left untouched.

The immediate family should be notified and asked to contact the Jewish undertaker. They will also contact the synagogue and set the ritual proceedings in motion. If no family are available the local Jewish undertaker or synagogue should be contacted for advice and help.

Where the death must be notified to the coroner or where the attending doctor is unable to complete the death certificate the immediate family should be informed and asked to contact their referred undertaker, who will be able to keep in contact with the coroner officer. Someone in authority should contact the local police station and ask for the duty inspector. He has a list of the coroners officers on call for each area, and will arrange for the appropriate coroners officer to communicate with the doctor.

The coroners officer are very helpful in expediting arrangements for Jewish bodies, so that the funeral need not be unduly delayed. Even in these circumstances there may not need to be a post-mortem.

The coroners officer should be informed that the body is Jewish and asked if:

*   The autopsy can be arranged for later that day or early next morning.

*   The result of the autopsy may be made available by the pathologist, by telephone, to the coroner.

*   The death certificate can be issued as soon as possible for burial preferably within 24 hours of death.

In case the ritual preparation of the body needs to be moved the family may use their chosen funeral director or the coroners officer will arrange for transport.

FUNERALS

Orthodox Jews are always buried but those of more liberal persuasion may choose cremation. There are usually separate Jewish burial grounds. The disposal of the Jewish dead is arranged by burial societies in the community. persons versed in the ritual are available usually through the appropriate synagogue to undertake the preparation of the dead for burial.

HINDUISM

DIET

Many Hindus do not eat meat, and some will not eat eggs. however, milk from cows is acceptable to most Hindus. Vegetarian Hindus cannot eat off a plate on which meat has been served, so nurses need to find an acceptable alternative - such as plastic plates - where requested.

CARE OF THE DYING

A devout Hindu who is very ill or dying may receive comfort from Hymns and readings from Hindu holy books, especially the Bhagavat. Gita. some may wish to lie on the floor, symbolising closeness to Mother Earth.

The patients family may wish to call a Hindu priest to perform holy rites and if no family is available the local Hindu temple may be approached for advice, if the patient wishes it.

The priest may tie a thread around the neck or wrist of the dying person to bless him or her. The priest may also sprinkle blessed water from the Ganges over the dying person, or place a scared tulsi leaf in his or her mouth.

The dying persons relative may also wish to bring money and clothes for him to touch before distribution to the needy. If they cannot go to the bedside themselves, they will appreciate it if a health care worker will do this for them.

Hindu patients very much wish to die at home. this has religious significance and death in hospital can cause great distress. All possible steps should be taken to enable the patient to go home to die - if this has been requested.

POST-MORTEM AND ORGAN TRANSPLANTS

There are no religious objections to blood transfusions or organ transplantation although permission must be obviously be sought. Post-mortem are also accepted although disliked

PROCEDURE AT DEATH

Funerals should ideally take place as soon as possible and in India would take place within 24 hours. In Britain there is likely to be a delay of several days because of pressure on crematorium services.

Under normal circumstances where a death certificate has been issued by the attending doctor the family should, if available be consulted before the body is handled, as distress may be caused if the body is touched by non-Hindus. the family will usually want to wash the body at home.

If no family is available the following procedure should be followed:

*   Wearing disposable gloves, close the eyes and straighten the limbs.

*   Jewellery, sacred threads and other religious objects should not be removed.

*   Wrap the body in a plain sheet, without religious emblem. In most cases it should not be washed as it is part of the funeral rites and will usually be carried out by relatives later.

The local Hindu community should be consulted for further advice.

In abnormal circumstances where for example the death must be reported to the coroner and there is a consequent delay, and the possibility of a post-mortem and the reasons for this must be carefully explained to the family, making sure they understand. the ritual preparation of the body can then commence after completion of the post-mortem.

FUNERALS

All adult Hindus are cremated but infants and young children may be buried.

Coping with the unfamiliar organisational side of death and cremation in Britain can be extremely distressing to bereaved relatives and careful explanation and practical help may be needed to contact undertakers and deal with the paperwork.

BUDDHISM

CARE OF THE DYING

Consideration for the dying will vary among the different Buddhist groups. Most important consideration relates to the state of mind at the time of death, as Buddhists believe that his will influence the character of rebirth.

The dying patient may seek the help of the hospital chaplain in arranging for a time of peace and quiet to allow for meditation, or may seek counselling from a fellow Buddhist. Some form of chanting may be used to influence the state of mind at death so that it may be peaceful.

Most Buddhist patients will be happy to give contact name and telephone number when they enter hospital.

POST-MORTEM AND ORGAN TRANSPLANTS

There is no objection to blood transfusion or organ transplants since helping others in fundamental to Buddhist belief. There is also no objection to a post-mortem.

PROCEDURE AT DEATH

Formal or ritualistic requirements in relation to a corpse are virtually nil. It is appropriate to follow normal hospital practise.

The most important thing when a Buddhist dies is that a Buddhist monk is informed as soon as possible and ideally he should be of the same school of Buddhism as the deceased.

FUNERALS

There are different schools of Buddhism in Britain each with different traditions. The usual time between death and disposal of the body is three to seven days.

Most Buddhists prefer cremation before burial and if the body or ashes buried, the headstone should bear the Buddhist symbol of the eight-spook wheel of law.

Where the rites cannot be observed any burial service may be used, but should make no reference to Christian doctrine or the deity and Christian prayers should be omitted.

A memory address should be given, or passage read from the Buddhist book, if available.

A visiting and counselling service usually is offered by local Buddhists and the Buddhist Hospice trust has recently been launched in Britain. For visiting counselling or general advise contact the local Buddhists.

BAHA'I FAITH

CARE OF THE DYING AND PROCEDURE AT DEATH

There is no ritual to be performed either prior to or after the death of an individual Baha'i. The nurse in attendance should act in accordance with the customary hospital procedures.

POST-MORTEM AND ORGAN TRANSPLANTS

There is no objection to blood transfusion, organ transplants or post-mortem.

FUNERALS

To satisfy Baha'i law two conditions must be fulfilled:

* Baha'is are always buried never cremated.

* The place of interment should be at a place within one hour's journey from the place of death.

Any undertaker may be used.

SIKHISM

CARE OF THE DYING

A dying Sikh may receive comfort from reciting hymns from Guru Grant Sa Hab, the holy Sikh book. If she or he is too ill to recite hymns than a relative or reader from the Sikh Gurdwara (temple) may do so instead. If no family members are present any practising Sikh may be asked to give help and religious comfort should it be requested by the patient.

POST-MORTEM AND ORGAN TRANSPLANTS

There are no objections by Sikhs to blood transfusion, organ transplants or post-mortem examination.

PROCEDURE AT DEATH

Generally Sikhs are happy for non-Sikhs to tend to the body and health workers may perform the normal last offices if the family wishes it. In Sikh tradition the family is responsible for all ceremonies and rites connected with death and many families will wish to wash and lay out the body themselves. If the family is available the following guidelines may be of help:

Under normal circumstances where a death certificate will be issued by the attending doctor special regard should be given to the five K's. In particular Kesh (unshorn hair) is felt to contribute to a Sikhs personality and should be left intact at all costs.

Do not trim the hair or beard. The hair on the head is sanctified at an initiation ceremony and should therefore be kept covered.

The face of the deceased may be displayed on numerous occasions prior to the funeral and a peaceful expression is desired. It is therefore appreciated if the face is cleaned, straightened if necessary and the eyes and mouth closed.

Limbs should also be straightened, and the body should be covered in a plain white sheet or shroud without religious emblem.

In abnormal circumstances where for example the attending doctor is unable to complete the death certificate or where the death for any reason must be reported to the coroner it is important to respect the five K's. Otherwise normal hospital procedures can be followed. The ritual proceedings will commence after autopsy.

It will however, be helpful if incisions made at autopsy are carefully sutured so that subsequent bathing and dressing does not cause wound dehiscence. Past experience has shown this phenomenon to cause distress to members of the family of the deceased.

FUNERAL

The body of a stillborn baby or late miscarriage should normally be given to the parents so that they can perform the normal funeral rites.

Apart from stillbirths and neonates who may be buried, Sikhs are always cremated. The cremation should take place as early as possible and in India would take place within 24 hours of death.

However, in Britain pressure on crematorium services makes this highly unlikely and the funeral may need to be delayed by days or weeks. Sikhs are cremated wearing five symbols of faith.

Coping with the unfamiliar organisational side of death and cremation in Britain can be extremely distressing to bereaved relatives, and careful explanation and practical help may be needed to contact undertakers and deal with the paperwork.

MUSLIM

Determination of Death: Since the introduction of advanced medical technology, besides the traditional definition of death which occurred when the heart and lungs stopped functioning, some Muslim schools of thought (mainly Sunni* and Shia* Muslims) have accepted brain death as a valid definition when the brain ceases to function, and brain cells begin to die. As such, artificial means may be used to preserve the body long enough to remove viable organs that are to be donated according to the conditions stated below.

Necessary to Life Interventions: It is permissible to use life support to save and lengthen life. Such equipment may not be disconnected for that will be construed as causing death. On the other hand, there is no obligation to continue these interventions just to prolong the imminent death. The purpose of aggressive medical intervention is to maintain the process of life, not to avoid or postpone death. It is forbidden to cause harm to the patient with equipment and drugs when the futility of such procedures is established by a medical team. Under those circumstances it is permissible to unplug life-support systems. "Mercy killing" or "Physician Assisted Aid in Dying" of terminally ill patients is prohibited.

Postmortem Examination: Autopsies performed for medical research and training is permissible. It is also permissible for determining the cause of death and for the discovery of new remedies. It is necessary to clearly explain the reasons for postmortem to the family. Donation of body parts or organs are allowed if there is a will to that effect or if the family permits. Blood transfusions are also permitted, including those from non-Muslims. Ritual preparation of the body is commenced after completion of the autopsy. Some families will wish to take their dead back to their country of origin for burial.

Death Rites: The dying Muslim patient may wish to sit or lie with his/her face towards Mecca and moving the bed if necessary, to make this possible is appreciated. Family members and elders in the community, including the Imam, may ask to be present so that they can provide moral support, religious guidance in matters of a living will, and to recite the Muslim scripture, the Koran, around the bed. A relative or another Muslim may whisper the call to prayer into the dying person's ear. In the case of the female client, the Imam and other male members of the community may come, but only if requested. As soon as death occurs the body should be covered completely and placed, if possible, with feet towards Mecca There are special procedures for washing and shrouding the body. Muslims are required by their religious law to prepare the body for burial. The body will be washed by the family. Men washed by other Muslim males and women by other Muslim females. Only when no community member can be contacted, may the health care providers perform these procedures. It is recommended that burial be performed as soon as possible, usually within 24 hours. Cremation is forbidden even if there is a will to that effect. The wife will be in mourning for three months. The funeral will take place at the Mosque within 24 hours. The Imam will conduct the prayer with women and men in separate rooms.

Residents Who Have No Next of Kin

1. Inform the GP as above.

2. If the will provides private payment contact the undertaker whom the resident has stated on their admission form. If not, contact the local authorities responsible for deceased without next of kin for their choice of undertakers.

Chapter 25

DEPUTY MANAGER JOB DESCRIPTION

Name:

Role: Deputy Manager in a Residential Home

Title: Deputy Manager

Responsible to: Manager and General Manager

Report to: Manager (In the absence of the Manger to the General

            Manager or Proprietor)

Minimum Qualifications: DBS Clearance, 2 years' experience in a senior role, to have or to work towards NVQ level 3 or 4. All mandatory courses completed. Knowledge of client group.

Aims of Post

- To deputise for Manager
- To implement approved care policy and legislations in the Home
- To co-ordinate the work of the staff
- To confer with GPs on the treatment of the clients
- To adhere to the aims and objectives of the Home

Key Tasks

4. Organise and maintain an efficient care service throughout the Home day and night in accordance with the National Care Standards 2000 and the Home's Policies and Procedures. Inform the manager of the implementation of such policy and aims/objectives.

5. Maintain contact with the community and clients and their relatives, by acting as the representative of the Home.

6. Maintain a high standard of client care in the Home and channels of communication which ensure that these standards are known and applied.

4. To have knowledge of and implement the National Care Standards, home life. Homes are for living in and the local authority procedures for protection of vulnerable adults.

Functions

23. Instructing and supervising staff as per job description on matters affecting the welfare of the clients. Documentation of

this to be kept in staff files. Observing the requirements of the National Care Standards and relevant legislation.

24. Maintaining records of clients.

25. Participating in ensuring clients nutritional needs and supervising the provision of special diets.

26. Ensure routines are followed by staff.

27. Assessing planning, implementing and evaluating the care plans of clients.

28. Participating in drug administration as per medication records.

29. Maintaining equipment and ensuring for the provision for repairs.

30. Instigating emergency repairs and advising the manager of such circumstances.

31. Preparing, receiving and giving reports as required.

32. Ensuring that all staff are familiar with fire prevention, precautions and have received proper instructions e.g. that staff are aware of the action they should take in the event of a fire. Ensure that all fire exits are kept clear and fire notices are permanently and prominently displayed at all times.

33. Participate in in-service training and induction programme for staff.

34. Inform the manager of any special training needs of staff.

35. Use the record of instruction and health and safety at work booklets.

36. Develop skills of other staff members.

37. Attend monthly staff meetings and in the absence of the manager chair the meetings.

38. Organise staff rota as required.

39. Ensure that daily, weekly routines are implemented.

40. Exercising leadership by personal example and maintaining morale of other staff members. Taking possible steps to safeguard the health, welfare and safety, clients, and their relatives in the Home introducing new members of staff to their duties and orientating them to the structure and geography of the Home, control and direct staff by good

leadership and example, counselling and supporting staff as required.

41. Monitor and inspect that work is carried out in accordance with agreed Policy.

42. Informing the manager, where appropriate, of accidents or complaints in the Home and assisting in investigating such incidents in accordance with the Home's Policy.

43. Arranging for safe-keeping of residents property, money and valuables according to the Home's Policy.

44. Co-operate with staff to keep the home clean, tidy and monitor such standards as a matter of routine.

Signature   date

Chapter 26

DISCIPLINARY WARNINGS

Name of member of Staff:

First Verbal Warning:

Appeal by Staff Member: Yes / No   Date Received:

Signed by Manager: Date:

Signed by Staff: Date:

Outcome of Appeal:

Second Verbal Warning: :

Appeal by Staff Member: Yes / No

 Date Received:

Signed by Manager: Date:

Signed by Staff: Date:

Outcome of Appeal:

First Written Warning:

Date Sent:

Brief Details:

Appeal by Staff Member: Yes / No Date Received:

Signed by Manager: Date:

Signed by Staff: Date:

Outcome of Appeal:

Final Written Warning:

Date Sent:

Brief Details:

Appeal by Staff Member: Yes / No   Date
Received:

Signed by Manager: Date:

Signed by Staff: Date:

Outcome of Appeal:

TERMINATION OF EMPLOYMENT

Date:

Reason for Leaving / Termination:

Total length of Service:

Appeal by Staff Member: Yes / No   Date
Received:

Signed by Manager: Date:

Signed by Staff: Date:

Outcome of Appeal:

Chapter 27

JOB DESCRIPTION DOMESTIC

Name: _____

Job Title: Domestic

Responsible: Registered Manager

Duties & Responsibilities

1. To ensure that the home is in a clean state at all times.

2. To ensure that the floors and carpets in every room are cleaned daily.

3. To ensure that all surfaces are dusted daily.

4. To ensure that toilets and bathrooms are cleaned daily, and the bath tubs, toilets and sinks are disinfected daily.

5. The inside of windows are kept clean.

6. To empty all dustbins and put refuse in appropriate bins.

7. To ensure that all chemicals are stores in the locked designated area.

8. To be familiar with control of substances hazardous to health (COSHH).

9. To observe the health and safety regulations.

10. To ensure that a safe environment is maintained at all times.

11. To provide a list of cleaning preparations for order every month.

12. To develop close working partnerships with other members of staff.

13. To report to Manager areas that cannot successfully be cleaned – e.g. faeces on chairs, carpets, odour problems.

14. Clean any marks off of bedroom chairs/ carpets etc,.

Signature Date:

Signature of Manager

Date:

Chapter 28

DRESS CODE FOR STAFF OF ALL HOMES

TROUSERS

The Proprietor is prepared to allow staff to wear trousers but they:

1. Must be of a smart appearance and be black or navy in colour.
2. No tracksuits, leggings or jeans are to be worn.

SKIRTS

1. Must be between knee and ankle level.
2. No wrap over skirts
3. No high splits
4. Must be dark in colour

SHIRTS

1. Must be clean and presentable

DRESSES

1. Must be presentable
2. Between knee and ankle level

BLOUSES

1. No vest tops or low-cut tops
2. Presentable

SHOES

1. No flip-flops or shoes without backings*
2. No high heels over 2 inches*
3. No platforms*
4. No sandals*
5. No trainers/boots*

    * = For Health and Safety Reasons

HATS

1. No hats to be worn on duty

JEWELLERY

Management will not accept liability for jewellery broken by residents.

1. Must not cause harm or injury to clients (will be classed as assault or abuse if this occurs)
2. Rings with raised stones must not be worn
3. Earrings/body piercings – management will not take responsibility if they cause/or are cause of injury.

COOK

Apart from a plain wedding band, we advise cooks not to wear rings. They harbour bacteria and can cause food poisoning. For food hygiene reasons cooks must wear gloves when handling food directly – e.g.: pastry making etc

Chapter 29

EMERGENCY AND CRISIS POLICY

Not all eventualities can be covered in this policy and so staff should refer to the relevant policy of the home where applicable. E.g. Accident Fire etc. If there was a Fire Flood or if for any other reason during the night the residents could return into the home. The resident may be taken by our mini-bus to any of its sisters homes (If they have vacancies). The placing boroughs Care Managers and next of kin must be notified immediately the next morning. Our Head Office has copies of next of kin Care Manager Details if the originals were destroyed.

If an emergency of the above name occurs during 9-5 pm then the placing authorities and next of kin must be notified for their consent of where their client is to be temporarily placed.

If a member of staff needs to go home whilst on duty due to sickness or to a personal crisis. The person in charge needs to ensure the home has adequate staff cover before the staff member leaves the home. The person on call or the manager must be notified.

If an event of the above nature occurs during the night, the manager or person on call is to be notified and to cover the shift themselves if necessary until alternative cover can be obtained.

Chapter 30

EMERGENCY ADMISSION TO HOSPITAL UNDER

THE MENTAL HEALTH ACT 1983

If a resident becomes acutely mentally unwell, the person in charge must first inform the client's CPN and psychiatrist and their advice sought. If the client does not have an allocated psychiatric team then the GP must be informed. If the resident exhibits violence in which the person in charge feels at any time that the client, the staff or other residents are in immediate danger the police must be informed immediately.

If it is the decision of the medical team that the client may need to be assessed under the Mental Health Act 1983. The approved social worker will co-ordinate for themselves and two doctors to visit (usually a psychiatrist and GP) to assess whether the client needs a hospital admission. The nearest relative is informed. If an admission is agreed by all parties, then the client will be encouraged to voluntarily be admitted to hospital. If the client refuses, the team will decide which section of the

Mental Health Act 1983 the client will be detained under Section 2 – would last for up to 28 days, on assessment to hospital and treatment may be given. Section 3 – would last up to 6 months and would entail treatment. Under these sections the client maybe taken against their will to hospital, although if they need to be physically restrained the police would have to be present to do this. The client would be escorted by the ASW to hospital via ambulance. The right to appeal is advised by the ASW. Staff would need to support the client and other residents and ensure that the disruption to them is minimal.

Guardianship Orders

Under Section 7 of the Mental Health Act 1983. A person may be told where to reside. A psychiatrist and approved social worker must agree it is in the person's best interests to live in a named place. NB The order must state an address, it cannot state "A Care Home".

The client under guardianship has the same rights to go out unescorted, and cannot be detained by others, as to prevent them to leave the premises. But if the person does not come back within a reasonable time, they are to be reported as missing to the police and social services.

The person does not have to comply with treatment and has the right to refuse medication the same as other clients.

Chapter 31

ENVIRONMENTAL POLICY

Although there is no current legislation for any business to have an environmental policy the Home is committed to ensuring we contribute to maintaining the environment. Therefore our organisation follows the Environmental Protection Act 1990, including the relevant Regulations under the Act.

All staff are educated and trained in environmental issues and the environmental effects of their activities and how to minimize waste and recycle packaging materials as much as possible.

The Home uses biodegradable chemicals where possible and recycles glass and paper which is collected by the local authority for recycling.

The Home also tries to minimize noise disturbances to our neighbours.

Chapter 32

EQUAL OPPORTUNITIES AND RACIAL HARASSMENT

The Home operates an equal opportunity policy in the employment of staff.

The Home provides a community service and is committed to ensuring equality of opportunity in employment and a high level of service to the people in the community. The aim of its equal opportunity policy is to ensure that no applicant or employee receives less favourable treatment on the grounds of sex, disability, social class, trade union activity, age, political or religious beliefs, race, colour, nationality, ethnic or national origins, marital status, having dependants, or their sexual orientation.

The Home recruitment procedure will ensure that all individuals are selected, promoted and treated on the basis of their relevant merits and abilities. All employees will be given equal opportunities and, where appropriate, special training to progress within the organisation. All forms of harassment, on the grounds listed above, are totally unacceptable to the home in its capacity as both employer and service provider.

The home is committed to a programme of action to make this policy fully effective and monitoring will be carried out.

The Home recruits from the multi-racial community it serves.

The admission and care of residents and reception given to all visitors is without prejudice towards sex, disability, social class, age, political or religious beliefs, race, colour, nationality, ethnic or national origins, marital status, having dependants, being lesbian or homosexual.

ANTI-OPPRESSIVE PRACTICE

Staff and clients should not feel oppressed and unable to voice their concerns or comments. The Home will endeavour to ensure all persons are given the opportunity to express their opinions.

RACIAL HARASSMENT

The Home will not tolerate Racial Harassment in any incidences.

Staff

With staff the disciplinary procedure will be used starting from final written warning and may be termination of their contract.

Visitors

Harassing staff, clients or other visitors – a written warning will be given and if it fails, the visitor will be banned from the premises.

Client – Harassing Staff

First instance a written warning will be given and/or intermediate review will be held.

If all attempts fail, then the Home will have no choice but to ask the client to be discharged.

Chapter 33

ESCORTING CLIENTS FOR HOSPITAL APPOINTMENTS;

The allocated member of staff is to ensure they are prepared properly when escorting clients to hospital. They must ensure:

1) They know what time and what type of transport has been arranged e.g. taxi or ambulance

2) The name of the hospital or resource centre they are going to

3) What department

4) What doctor they are to see

5) The reason why the client is attending the hospital

6) Any history relating to the purpose of the appointment e.g. rectal bleeding, mole on left arm, etc. For how long the symptoms have been present and what treatments the GP may have already tried.

The escort must be confident that they can answer any queries the doctors may ask.

The medication profile and present MAR Sheet are to be taken to the appointment. If it is a first appointment to this department then a copy of the client's medical history must be taken.

Take a pen and some paper in order to make notes.

The escort is to go into see the doctor with the client, unless the client specifically objects. If the client does object to your presence and you feel there is some information the client will not tell the doctor, request to speak to the doctor before the client has their consultation.

The name of the doctor is to be requested and his/her title – e.g. consultant, registrar, senior house officer. So if there are any queries later on we have a named contact.

Any medication changes must be entered on the Medication Profile by the doctor and a prescription must be given to the escort.

If another appointment is to be made after the consultation, book transport by ambulance, if that was the means of transport you used that day. When you return to the Home all of the following information must be documented in the daily care notes:

a) whom the client saw at the hospital, name of doctor
b) What department
c) For what reasons
d) Any instructions the doctor gave
e) Any medication changes – drug name, dose and frequency
f) Date of next appointment (if one made)
g) Sign your name in full where you finish writing

Write the date of any next appointment in the diary.

Chapter 34

RECORD OF FIRE DRILL

- List staff present
- Where pretence fire is
- Where all residents are
- State which bedrooms they are in or which lounge etc
- Which residents are out
- Who refused to leave premises or was non-compliant with drill
- Did anyone fall or have an accident during drill
- How long did evacuation take?
- Who took roll call

Chapter 35

IN CASE OF FIRE

A Fire Risk Assessment has been carried out and a Fire Procedure developed. There is an appropriate recording system maintained.

Any persons who discovers a fire, sees smoke, or smells unusual fumes should take the following action:

Any person who discovers a fire, sees smoke, or smells unusual fumes should take the following action:

1.Sound the Alarm by operating the nearest alarm call point i.e. by breaking the glass. Please see section 9 below for the positions of the call points. Take with you a copy of the roll call list located by each of the call points.

2The person in charge should telephone the Fire Brigade by dialling 999. Give the name, address and telephone number of the Home.

3.Ask all able Residents to leave the premises via the fire exit (see section 10 for the location of the fire exits). Rescue Residents from immediate danger, remove all persons in immediate danger of fire or smoke to the nearest safe area, then to the outside of the Home. The lift must not be used.

4.Confine the Fire - Close door to room in which fire or smoke is detected, to prevent spread of fire.

5.Secure the Area - Close all doors and windows in vicinity of fire. Shut off all electrical, gas and oxygen equipment in vicinity of fire.

6.Attempt to Extinguish Fire - If the fire is of a size of a waste-basket or smaller, use fire extinguishers to control or extinguish fire. Do not endanger yourself or others. See section 11 for the location of the fire extinguishers.

7.Keep Calm - Do not Panic. Remain calm and reassure all residents.

8.Consult specific fire instructions which were given to you at time of employment.

Below is an example of typical care home

9.Location of call points

•Kitchen

by back door

•Ground floor hallway -

on wall by the front door

•Ground floor lounge -

191

on wall by French doors

•First floor   -

hallway at top of stairs

10) Location of the Fire Exits

- Ground floor kitchen   -   Back door
- Smokers' room   -
- Lounge   -French doors
- Dining room   -
- First floor   -   Front
  doors

11.   *Location of the Fire Extinguishers*

Location of Gas Mains (Shut Off Point)

Under stairs cupboard on the ground floor.

Procedure: Pull handle down to shut off.

Location of Electric Mains (Shut Off Point)

This is located on the ground floor in the hallway, behind the front door.

Chapter 36

FIRST AID

First aid is the immediate care given to a sick or injured person before health-care professionals arrive. Its aims are to preserve life, prevent a condition from worsening, and promote as fast a recovery as possible. Your top priority in emergency situations, before starting first aid, is to call 999 for medical assistance. If possible, ask a bystander to make the call. The next priority is to check the scene for possible dangers to you, the victim, or bystanders, such as fire or dangerous fumes. You will not be able to help the person if you become a victim yourself, so you should always put your own safety first. If you cannot approach the victim safely phone for help immediately. If it is safe to approach, you should then aim to assess the victim's condition and give first aid.

The instructions in this section are designed to help you handle common emergency situations. There is no substitute for professional training, however, and the best form of training is a practical course in first aid. The British Red Cross, St John Ambulance, and St Andrew's Ambulance Association all run courses. On successful completion of a first aid course, you receive a certificate that is valid for 3 years. Training in some skills, such as artificial respiration, is valid for 1 year.

ABC of resuscitation

Oxygen is vital for life. Normally, it is taken in by breathing and circulates around the body in the bloodstream. If either breathing or circulation fail, a procedure called resuscitation must be performed to supply the body with oxygen. The procedure is based on three checks known as the ABC of resuscitation: "ABC" stands for Airway, Breathing and Circulation. If a person is unconscious, always follow the ABC sequence before giving any other treatment. You need to open the airway; establish if the victim is breathing; and assess whether the blood is circulating for a pulse and other signs, such as normal skin colour. If the victim is not breathing, you must give artificial respiration to breathing, you must give artificial respiration to breathe oxygen into the body. If there is no pulse or other signs of circulation, you must start cardiopulmonary resuscitation (CPR).

Action in an emergency

When faced with an emergency, you should always work to a clear plan, staying calm and controlled so that you can act effectively. Take several deep, slow breaths to help you calm down, if necessary. If possible, you should send someone for an ambulance while you deal with the situation. Before trying to help the victim you must be certain that you are not putting yourself in any possible danger. Remember that you will not be able to help anyone else if you become a victim yourself. Very simple measures, such as turning off an electrical switch, may be enough to eliminate danger. After to have made sure that the scene is safe, the next step is to check the victim's condition and carry out the appropriate first-aid treatment. Treat multiple injuries in order of priority, dealing with life-threatening conditions first.

Recovery position

The recovery position is a secure position in which to place who is unconscious victim is left lying on his or her back, the tongue may block the throat and prevent air from reaching the airways to the lungs. This situation is life-threatening because the breathing and heartbeat may stop. The recovery position keeps the head, neck and back aligned, keeps the airway open, and allows fluid to drain out of the mouth if the victim vomits. You may not need to follow all of the steps shown below if the person is found lying on his or her front or side.

Artificial respiration

Artificial respiration is a way to force your exhaled air into the lungs of a person who is not breathing. If breathing has stopped, the victim will be unconscious, the chest will not rise or fall, and you will not be able to feel or hear breath. The face may be greyish blue. In this situation, you must give artificial respiration immediately – your exhaled air still contains enough oxygen to sustain the victim's vital organs until help arrives. If the pulse is absent, you need to carry out cardiopulmonary resuscitation – artificial respiratory combined with chest compressions. When giving artificial respiration to an infant, be careful not to blow too hard or air will go into the stomach. Use a face shield or mask, if available. However, even if you do not have one, do not hesitate to help a victim.

Adult

1. If you have a helper, ask him or her to call an ambulance. If you are alone and the victim is an adult, call an ambulance before proceeding to Step 2. If the victim is a child, go to Step 2 immediately.

2. Lay the victim on his or her back. Remove anything that is obviously loose, such as dentures, from the mouth. Open the airway by pressing down on the forehead with one hand lifting the chin with two fingers of you other hand. If you suspect spinal injury, try to lift the chin gently without the tilting the head, or tilt the head only slightly.

3. Pinch the victim's nose closed with your thumb and index finger. Take a deep breath, then place you open mouth to make a good seal. Blow air into the victim's mouth for about 1 ½ seconds.

4. Lift your mouth away, keeping your hands in place to maintain the victim's head position. Glance at the victim's chest; you should see the chest fall as air leaves the lungs. Take a

breath yourself, then give another 1 ½ second breath.

5. Look at the victim's chest again. If there is no rise and fall, check the head position and ensuring that you make good seal around the mouth. If the chest still does not move, assume that the airway is blocked and treat as for choking. If the chest does rise and fall, go to Step 6.

6. Check the pulse. If it is absent, start CPR. If there is a pulse or other signs of circulation, continue artificial respiration; give 1 minute if this has not already been done. Check for a pulse after every minute. If the victim starts breathing, place him or her in the recovery position.

CHOKING

Choking is due to obstruction of the airway. In adults; a common cause of choking is food stuck in the throat.

1. Encourage the victim to cough. If this does not dislodge the object, bend the person forwards and give the back 5 sharp slaps between the shoulder blades.

2. If the victim continues to cough without clearing the object, you will need to give abdominal thrusts. Stand behind the victim and reach

around the body. Make a fist with one hand. Position the thumb side of your fist in the middle of the abdomen, just below the breastbone.

3. Place you other hand over your fist, and pull sharply inwards and upwards. Give 5 of these thrusts. If the object is not disclosed, repeat this cycle of 5 thrusts. If the victim continues to choke or loses conscious adults,

Conscious adults

1. Encourage the victim to cough. If this does not dislodge the object, bend the person forwards and give the back 5 sharp slaps between the shoulder blades.

2. If the victim continues to cough without clearing the object, you will need to give abdominal thrusts. Stand behind the victim and reach around the body. Position the thumb side of your fist in the middle of the abdomen, just below the breastbone.

3. Place you other hand over your fist, and pull sharply inwards and upwards. Give 5 of these

thrusts. If the object is dislodged, repeat this cycle of 5 slaps and 5 thrusts. If the victim continues to choke or loses consciousness, call an ambulance.

Unconscious adults

1. If you have a helper, send him or her to call an ambulance. Lay the victim down on a firm surface and open the airway by pressing the forehead down with one hand and lifting the chin with two fingers of the other. Remove any obvious obstruction from the mouth.

2. If the victim is not breathing, attempt up to 5 slow breaths of artificial respiration. If the chest does not move (a sign that air is not reaching the lungs), turn the victim on his or her side and give up to 5 sharp back slaps between the shoulder blades. Check the mouth again. If unsuccessful, proceed to step 3.

3. Turn the victim onto his or her back. Kneel astride the victim, and place the heel of one hand just above the navel. Lay your other hand on top with the fingers raised. Thrust quickly inwards and upwards up to 5 times. Check the mouth again. If the victim is not breathing, give another 5 breaths of artificial respiration. If unsuccessful, continue the cycle of back slaps

and artificial respiration until medical help arrives.

4. If the victim starts breathing again, place him in the recovery position and monitor the breathing and pulse regularly until medical help arrives.

Cardiopulmonary Resuscitation CPR);
CPR is a life-saving technique in which artificial respiration is combined with chest compressions. It is performed on an unconscious victim who is not breathing and has no pulse, to keep the blood circulating and ensure that the oxygen supplied by artificial respiration reaches the brain and other vital organs. Do not stop giving CPR until the victim's heart starts beating or medical help arrives. If you are too tired to continue, try to find another trained person to take over from you until medical help arrives. When giving chest compressions to children slightly less pressure is used in order to avoid injury and they are also given at a slightly different rate in children and it is important not to blow too hard, especially when treating an infant.

Adults

1. Call an ambulance. Lay the victim face upwards on hard surface. Open the airway by placing one hand on the forehead to tilt the head back and lifting the chin with two fingers of the other. Look at the chest for signs of breathing and feel for the breath on you cheek.

2. If the victim is not breathing, pinch the nostrils shut with one hand, keep the chin tilted with the other. Seal your mouth over the victim's mouth, and give 2 breaths of artificial respiration. Pause to take a breath yourself between giving breaths.

3. Check the pulse at the neck for up to 10 second and look for other signs of recovery, such as return of skin colour or breathing. If you cannot find a pulse, continue artificial respiration. If you cannot find a pulse and there are no signs of recovery, begin CPR.

4. Kneel to one side of the victim. Using the hand farthest from the victim's head, slide your fingers along the lowest rib to where it meets the breastbone. Place your middle finger on this point and your index finger just above it.

5. Place the heel of your other hand on the breastbone, just above your index finger. This

is area of the chest where you must apply the compressions.

6. Lift the fingers of the first away and lay the hand on top of your other hand. Interlock the fingers of the bottom hand are lifted off the chest.

7. Kneel upright with your shoulders directly above the victim and your elbows locked straight. Press downwards, depressing the breastbone 4-5cm (1 ½ - 2in), then release the pressure without moving your hands. Compress the chest in this chest way 15 times at a rate of about 15 compressions in 10 seconds, maintaining an even rhythm. Then give 2 breaths or artificial respiration.

Continue giving cycles of 15 chest compressions with 2 breaths of artificial
   Respiration;

After 4 cycles of compressions and breaths check them again   every few minutes thereafter. If they are absent, continue CPR. If the pulse   and breathing return, stop CPR but continue to monitor the pulse and breathing   until help arrives.

Shock;

Shock can occur as a result of any severe injury or illness that dramatically reduces the flow of blood around the body, such as a heart attack or severe bleeding. It can also be due to loss of body fluids from burns or severe diarrhoea and vomiting. If shock is not treated rapidly, pulse; grey-blue skin, especially on the lips; sweating; and cold, clammy skin. Later, excessive thirst and nausea and vomiting may occur. The victim may feel weak or dizzy and development rapid, shallow breathing and a faint pulse. He or she may be restless, gasp for air, and eventually lose consciousness. It is essential to call for medical help at the first signs of shock, and to keep the victim warm and comfortable.

1. If you have a helper, send him or her to call an ambulance. Treat any obvious cause of shock, such as severe bleeding

2. Of the person is breathing normally, lay him or her down. If you suspect a fracture, keep the person flat. Otherwise, raise the legs above the level of the heart. If the person is having difficulty in breathing, help him or her to sit in a comfortable position.

3. Loosen any restrictions around the neck, chest, and waist, and remove the victim's shoes. Call an ambulance if a helper has not already done so.

4. Stop the victim becoming cold by covering him or her with a blanket. Check the victim's level of consciousness by asking simple, direct questions. Monitor breathing and pulse and be prepared to resuscitate if necessary

Anaphylactic shock

Anaphylactic shock is a life-threatening allergic reaction to a specific food, drug, or insect sting. It can develop within second or a few minutes. The victim may be anxious and may have puffy eyes, a swollen face, lips, and tongue, and an itchy, red skin rash. He or she may develop wheezing and severe breathing difficulties and may lose consciousness. An injection of epinephrine (adrenaline) and oxygen must be given as quickly as possible. If the person is aware of having an allergy and carries a supply of epinephrine, you can help him or her to use this supply. Otherwise, first aid is limited to keeping the person comfortable and, if necessary, helping him or her to breathe until medical help arrives.

1. Call an ambulance or send a helper to do so immediately. If possible, provide the emergency services with details of the cause of the allergic reaction.

2. If the victim is conscious, help him or her to sit up in the position that makes breathing easiest.

3. Check if the victim is carrying a syringe of epinephrine (adrenaline). Help him or her to use it, or administer it yourself if you have been trained.

4. If the person loses consciousness, open the airway, check breathing and pulse, and be prepared to carry out resuscitation if necessary (see ABC of resuscitation, p.290). Monitor the person's pulse and breathing until medical help arrives.

Chapter 37

FOOD SAFETY

(more details in food hygiene chapter)

As per the Food Safety Act of 1990 all staff who handle food must have basic food hygiene training verified by an external nominated body.

All food prepared by staff, staff must wash their hands regularly with an anti-bacterial soap in a separate hand washing sink and dried either by a disposable towel or hand drier.

All food prepared must be cut using colour co-ordinated chopping boards e.g. White – bakery, Blue – raw fish, Red – raw meat, Brown – vegetables, Yellow – cooked meats.

All opened foods stored in the fridge must be covered and labelled with the date opened and what the dish contains.

No opened cans must be stored in the fridge.

Raw meats must be stored at the bottom area of the fridge (to avoid dripping blood etc contaminating other foods).

Joints of meat must be probed in the middle by a thermometer to ensure they are cooked thoroughly. The temperate must be over 75°C. All other foods that may cause food poisoning must be probed before being served to a temperature of at least 15°C. All these temperatures must be recorded. Soup must be served at 60°C, to avoid scalding if spilt.

Delivery of Foods

When frozen foods are delivered to the Home a random sample of meat contained food must be probed to ensure the temperature is within -16°C to -17°C. These tests must be documented.

Fried/Freezers Temperatures

The fridge temperature must be maintained at 5°C. The freezer maintained at -18°C

The temperature must be taken and recorded at least once daily – when the doors have not been opened for over 2 hours.

Protective Clothing

Must be worn over clothes which have been worn to work as to avoid cross contamination. All open wounds must be covered with a blue plaster.

Infectious Diseases

Persons who have had diarrhoea/vomiting must not return to work until they have had no further symptoms for 48 hours.

Chapter 38

FOOD TEMPERATURE BOOK

DATE	TIME	NAME OF FOOD	TEMP	SIGNATURE

Chapter 39

GIFTS AND GRATUITIES & BEQUESTS

Under no circumstances are staff allowed to accept or expect tips or gifts from residents or their representatives. Although at Christmas a gift of no more than £10.00 in value may be accepted on behalf of all staff and residents e.g. tin of sweets, biscuits etc.

The management must be informed if any resident or visitor offers staff a gift or money the resident will be reminded of the contents of this policy and this must be entered into the relevant persons daily care notes.

Staff are not to give individual residents presents from themselves. The home will purchase a present for residents at Christmas and birthdays. All gifts given to residents will be of equal monetary value.

The next of kin will be notified if the resident persistently offers gifts to the staff or other persons.

It is not acceptable for staff of any grade to be included in, or to benefit from bequests from a former resident.

Staff must never be involved in any legal matters involving residents, i.e. witnessing wills or agreeing to be executor to such/similar documents.

Chapter 40

GUIDELINES TO COMPLETING RESIDENT REVIEW FORM

Reviews;

Once the individual has become an established resident, a programmed of regular reviews to monitor the clients care plan and progress. To ensure the resident is satisfied with the home should be agreed and the purpose of the review explained.

Dental Needs;

Does the client have own teeth, top or bottom denture?

Who cleans them?

Name of dentist?

Date last seen by dentist?

Is it a domiciliary visit?

Who arranges these appointments?

Optician's client diabetic? Does ophthalmology department at local hospital see them?

Does the client wear spectacles all the time, or just for reading? Does the client have cataracts/glaucoma?

Date of last S/B optician?

Name of optician?

Who arranges the appointments?

Hearing

Can the client hear in both ears?

Does the client wear a hearing aid?

Who puts it in?

Who organizes batteries for the hearing aid?

Where is their "Hearing Department"?

When did they last visit?

Does client have regular syringing?

Chiropody;

Is the client diabetic?

Who cuts the client's toenails?

If chiropodist, why?

Date of last visit?

Frequency?

Domiciliary or hospital

Religious Needs;

Is client practicing a religion?

Does clergy visit?

Does client go to mass?

Who takes them?

Who arranges this?

Day Care/Activities;

Does the client go to a day Centre?

What Centre?

Which days?

How do they get there?

Who organizes their transport?

Is day care formal or informal?

What do they do at the Centre?

Are they attending day Centre enough or too often?

What activities does the resident participate in there?

Do they prefer individual or group activities?

What activities does the client participate in the home or outside?

Unfulfilled Ambitions

Is there an ambition that the client would like to fulfill?

Any person/place they would like to see?

Who will assist them to fulfill these?

Social and Family Contacts;

How does the client get on with other residents?

Are there particular residents they like or dislike?

How do they get on with staff?

How do they get on with visitors to the home?

Do family/friends visit?

Frequency

Do family/friends participate in care?

Does client visit family/friends?

Physical Health;

Has this improved or deteriorated within the last six months?

Any health complaints?

Name of GP?

Name of any doctors seen at the hospital and reason

Any operations or hospital appointments within last six months

Has the client been seen by the District Nurse?

Has the client got Hypertension, thyroid, problems etc.

Any blood tests taken and results

Psychological/Mental Health;

How has mental health stabilized/improved/deteriorated within the last six months?

Name of psychiatrist?

Where is he/she based?

Frequency of visits?

Does staff escort them?

Does CPN visit?

Frequency and reason?

List of Present Medication

Any change within the last six months?

Who Reviews Medication

GP to review physical medication every 6 months

Personal Finance and Expenditure

Who provides personal expenditure?

Who pays fees?

Are Fees up to date?

List how fee is made up?

Where does it come from e.g. Council, Self?

How much is it per week?

On what day of the week is it given?

Does client need to go to the bank periodically to put excess away or does the client give it to a relative for safekeeping?

Clothing

Does the client need new clothing?

If they go out in winter – have they enough warm clothing?

Who is to provide finance?

Who will get the new clothes

Bedroom

Single or shared?

Which floor?

What facilities are in the room?

Does the client like the room?

Is there anything they want or want changed in their room?

Do they use lift by themselves (if applicable) or do they need staff assistance?

Any changes to the room, e.g. decorating, new bedding purchased etc. Suggestions and Comments Raised by Client Anything that the client wants to raise?

Are they happy times at the home?

Risk Identified

List what risk assessments are in place.

Comment on these.

Independence and Choice

How does the client exercise their independence choice?

How can this be encouraged?

Chapter 41

HANDLING RESIDENTS FINANCE

Residents should be encouraged to maintain control over their own financial affairs, if possible. If they are unable to do so this should be dealt with by relatives or another person outside the Home – either as an agent or appointee. If one is unable to carry out this task the Care Manager who placed the client will be notified and the relevant placing authority will be asked to act as an appointee. An application to the Court of Protection can be made if the client has sufficient funds to pay for this service.

If the client is able, they may wish to give a relative or friend Power of Attorney.

The proprietor, or staff employed by the Home, must not have Power of Attorney or be a receiver under Court of Protection. If the person has no-one to be an appointee and the placing authority cannot offer this service, the owner, as a last resort, will act as the appointee. The Home will collect the pension or benefit (the next of kin, if applicable, and CSCI will be notified of this). The amount cashed each week by the benefit books will be recorded and the amount paid towards the fees. The remainder as personal allowance will be dealt with as follows:-

- The balance will be signed and witnessed by the appointee and senior staff, if the resident in unable or unwilling to do so.

- All monies transacted on behalf of residents will be accompanied by a receipt. This receipt will be numbered and should correspond with the account form.

Monetary transactions may arise for a number of reasons and will be recorded as previously mentioned e.g.:

a) looking after personal allowances

b) monies given to the Home on behalf of residents, their relatives or friends

c) full or part payment of fee

d) payment for additional services (hairdressing, clothing, toiletries, cigarettes, etc.

If for any reason a resident is lent money by the Home, e.g. in lieu of delayed benefit payment, the amount must be shown as a debit entry under the heading balance until it is repaid.

Records of all transactions will be shown to the next of kin or person chosen by the client, so they can see how the account is being operated. This designated person will sign on the account record when they visit.

Accumulating monies of over £300.00 will be placed into the resident's own bank account. The account will be in the name of the resident and/or their appointee. Interest should be credited on a regular basis.

Any arrangements for handling residents' finances will be clearly stated in the care plan.

Chapter 42

Health & Safety

All Employees

The Health and Safety at Work Act 1974 states:

"It shall be the duty of every employee while at work"

a) to take reasonable care for the health and safety of himself and of any other persons who may be affected by his acts or omissions at work, and

b) as regards any duty or requirement imposed on his employer or any other person by or under any of the relevant statutory provisions, to co-operate with him so far as is necessary to enable that duty or requirement to be performed or complied with"

The Act also states:

"No person shall intentionally or recklessly interfere with or misuse anything provided in the interests of health, safety or welfare in pursuance of any of the relevant statutory provisions".

In order that the laws be observed and the responsibilities to residents and other visitors to the Home are carried out ALL employees are expected:

a) To know the special safety measures and arrangement to be adopted in their own working areas and to ensure they are applied.

b) To observe standards of dress consistent with safety and/or hygiene. Suitable footwear with non-slip soles must be worn.

c) To exercise good standards of housekeeping and cleanliness.

d) To know and apply the emergency procedures in respect of fire and first aid.

e) To use and not wilfully misuse, neglect or interfere with things provided for his own safety and/or the safety of others.

f) To co-operate with the Owners and other employees in promoting improved safety measures in the Home.

g) To ensure that they are shown and use the correct methods when lifting residents, including the correct methods to be used in confined spaces, to obtain the help of another person whenever necessary, and to use lifting apparatus provided whenever necessary.

h)   Not wear rings, other than a wedding or signet ring.

i)   To ensure that wet or dirty floors are washed and dried without delay.

j)   To ensure that after washing/bathing residents or dealing or dealing with soiled clothing, hands are washed to prevent infection, and protective gloves are worn of any cuts or scratches are present.

k)   To read and comply with the instructions for use of cleaning products, and other substances hazardous to health, contained in the COSHH File.

Residents

The residents are expected:

a)   To exercise responsibility for the safety of self and other residents.

b)   To observe standards of dress consistent with safety and/or hygiene when helping in the Home.

c)   To observe all the safety rules of the Home and in particular the instructions of care staff given in an emergency.

d)   To use and not wilfully, neglect or interfere with things provided for his/her safety.

Note

All residents and their families should be made aware of the contents of this section.

Visitors

Regular visitors and other users of the premises (e.g. delivery men from specific companies), should be required to observe the safety rules of the Home.

Contractors

Contractors must adhere to the Home's Policy on Health and Safety and must have their own Public Liability Insurance. They must tell the person in charge when they arrive on the premises, the person in charge must check the area which the trade person is working before, during and after the works are complete to ensure the Home's Policy is being adhered to

C.O.S.H.H.

What are C.O.S.H.H Regulations?

They are regulations covering Control of Substances Hazardous to Health. Came into force on 1st October 1989.

What are Substances Hazardous to Health?

1. These are substances labelled

   * corrosive

   * irritant

   * harmful

* Toxic

   * Very toxic

2. Pesticides and any other chemicals

3. Products or by products (dust, fumes, etc.)

4. Microorganisme (virussés, bactérie, etc.)

5. Carcinogens (cancer causing agents)

An Employee's Responsibilities under C.O.S.H.H are:-

1. Taking part in training programmes

2. Practising safe working practices

3. Reading container labels telling you about health risks and other hazards.

4. Reporting any hazard or defect to your manager

5. Using Personal Protective Equipment correctly - learn to use and inspect equipment.

6. Taking part in Health Surveillance.

7. Storing equipment properly.

8. Using control measures correctly and the intended manner for materials, plants, etc.

Instruction & Training Programmes are a Vital Part of C.O.S.H.H.

1.Learn how C.O.S.H.H. requirements affect you, your colleagues and your employer.
2.Learn about chemicals and other substances you use at work with a focus on health risks.
3.Look at your policies and programmes for health and safety.
4.Control measures and safe work practices that protect you from hazardous substances.
5.Read labels and understand the precautions you must take.
6.For all accidents involving C.O.S.H.H. products, follow the first aid procedures as per the C.O.S.H.H. data sheet. Take a copy for the medics if you require medical attention.

ELECTRICITY AT WORK
Electricity at Work Regulations 4 (27/989)
Electricity can kill, Most deaths are caused by contact with overhead or underground cables – which we, as working in residential care, may not be applicable, but even non-fatal shocks can cause severe and permanent injuries.

Shocks from faulty equipment may lead to falls, poor electrical installations and faulty appliances can lead to fires, which may also cause death or injury to others. The Home will inspect and test all electrical appliances annually or when residents bring into the Home any electrical items.

Any competent trained person can test the equipment it does not have to be carried out by an electrician, but the following guidelines should be followed.

Look at the appliances – the cable and plug after disconnection, are there signs of:

1)   Damage – cuts to the cable covering

2)   Damage to the plug – e.g. the casing is cracked, or the pins bent

3)   Non-standard joints including taped joints in the cable

4)   The outer covering of the cable not being gripped where it enters the plug or equipment. Look to see if the coloured insulation of the internal wires are showing.

5)   Damage to the outer cover of the equipment or obvious loose screws or parts.

6)   Signs of overheating – burn marks or straining

In addition the plug cover should be removed and checked for the following:

1) That a fuse is being used and that it is the correct one

2) The cord grip is holding the outer part of the cable tightly

3) The wires are correctly fitted (as attached)

4) No bare wire is visible

5) Terminal screws are tight

6) No sign of overheating

This does not apply to moulded plugs where only the fuse can be checked. Most of the checks also apply to extension leads and their plugs and sockets.

Each appliance is about to be plugged into the portable appliance tester and switched on, this will indicate whether the appliance passes or fails this test. All appliances which fail the plug must be removed and reported to the manager or proprietor.

All appliances will be labelled accordingly – pass or fail with the date and signature of person carrying out the check.

A record of each item checked should be kept in the folder, labelled: electricity at work.

Electric mains will be tested every five years by a qualified electrician.

Chapter 43

IDENTITY AND DIGNITY OF RESIDENTS

Staff need to question their own practice as to ensure clients identity and dignity are maintained.

1. Are all members of staff given the opportunity to develop mutually trusting relationships with residents?

2. Is each resident addressed by their surname and formal title until they indicate the wish to be addressed in another way?

3. Where appropriate is each resident included in discussions about their conditions? Alternatively is there a room available away from residents for confidential discussion by staff?

4. Are care assistants actively encouraged to devote time to get to know their residents as individuals whilst carrying out their duties?

5. Do staff recognise and provide for the different interests and cultural background of each resident?

6. Are care assistants sure that each resident is offered privacy when attending to personal needs?

Some points to consider are:

1. When tending to a resident all opportunities should be used to show interest in, and awareness of, him/her as a person by establishing and maintaining a mutually trusting relationship.

2. A resident should be addressed by his proper name and title. Some residents may prefer to be known by a first name or a familiar pet name, but this should be used only in response to their expressed preference and with their permission.

3. Discussions should include the resident and take place in a private room away from the other residents.

4. When a care assistant is attending to a resident there is an advantage in working alone in order to get to know him/her as an individual. Assistance can be requested if it is necessary.

5. The resident's personal property such as toothbrush, dentures, spectacles and clothes should be clearly marked with his/her name as to avoid items being mislaid.

6. Bibs are associated, by most old people, with baby care and dependency and should never be used.

7. Privacy should be ensured for purposes of treatment, dressing and for use of the WC or commode.

Chapter 44

FIVE DAY INDUCTION PROGRAMMES

MONDAY

Report to work from 9.30am to 4.00pm which is the middle shift.

a) The inductor or manager welcomes him/her.

b) Show him/her the staff room, changing room and WC.

c) Introduce him/her to the rest of staff on duty.

d) Take him/her to the office and offer a cup of tea/coffee.

e) Have about ten minutes' informal chat, e.g., weather, news, politics, etc.

f) Give him/her the induction programme, contract, record of instructions, check list, routine health and safety.

g) Take him/her round the outline or geography of the home, showing all equipment with emphasis on fire equipment.

h) Introduce him/her to the residents.

i) Spend part of the morning working with the staff.

j) Spend part of the day talking to the residents.

k)   The inductor should learn more about the employee's past experience in the job, hobbies, etc.

l)   It should be noted that the residents' rights and privacy are respected.

TUESDAY

Report for the morning shift (7.30am to 2.15pm).

a)   Part of the morning is spend working with the staff in order to know the a.m. routine.

b)   He/she should be given 30 minutes to go round the home him/herself to become familiarised with the geography of the home, and location of fuses, gas and electricity mains.

c)   Show how to do different types of lifting.

d)   Spend about one hour with the residents either chatting or playing a game.

e)   Discuss fire precautions, i.e., procedures in the event of fire, fire prevention, how to use all fire equipment, e.g., extinguishers, fire blanket, fire zones, how to evacuate residents, location of fire exits, how to sound the fire alarm.

f) Go through one quarter of the residents' care plans.

g) Go over how to take a resident's pulse, temperature, respiration and blood pressure.

WEDNESDAY

Work afternoon shift (2.00pm-8.30pm) to learn the routine - half of the day.

a) Discuss care plans of one quarter of the residents.

b) 30 minutes in laundry room in order to learn how the washing machine, drier, etc., operate and how to deal with the washing.

c) Spend 30 minutes in the kitchen and larder with the cook to learn how to use the equipment, e.g., dish washer, cooker, microwave, etc., and the routine to keep the kitchen tidy. Also the stock taking records, recording of menu and environmental health requirements.

d) How to make the beds.

e) Domestic/cleaning procedures, use of vacuum cleaner, etc.

f) Discussion on sexual harassment, discrimination, equal opportunities.

THURSDAY

Work a long day, i.e., 7.30am to 8.30pm which covers administration.

a) Go through some of the home policies.

b) How to deal with official and unofficial visitors to the home.

c) How to use the lift.

d) How to deal with emergency first aid, e.g., falls, unconsciousness, heart attack.

e) If a resident goes missing or suddenly becomes ill.

f) If the employee is in a senior position: how to deal with ordering, giving out and recording drugs.

g) How to write reports in the care notes.

h) Emphasis on the confidentiality of the home.

i) Equal opportunities.

j) Procedure for handover.

k) What to do when staff phone in sick.

l) Disposal of contaminated waste and general sharp objects.

FRIDAY

The employee should do a full shift from 8.00pm to 8.00am in order to learn about the night routine.

a) Go through the contract and have him/her sign it, sickness, benefit, holidays.

b) Obtain his/her P45 or P46.

c)   Care of dying.

d)   Health and Safety.

e)   Feedback

f)   Employee to sign induction programme to confirm that induction has been given.

The employee is encouraged to ask questions at any time whilst he/she is working.

Appraisal is done after one month, then 3 months, then 6 months, after which time yearly appraisals should be carried out.

Chapter 45

INFECTION CONTROL - PROCEDURE

All staff are accountable for their own actions and must adhere to the following safe practices as to minimise cross-infection and protect themselves and other clients.

Staff should follow good basic hygiene and practice; routine hand-washing, as per "Essential Steps" Guidelines.

1. Before and after each shift

2. Before and after each break

3. After handling contaminated items

4. After using the toilet

5. Before eating and drinking

6. Before handling food

7. After smoking

8. Before and after assisting clients with each activity.

Procedure

1. Wet the hands up to the wrists before applying sanitizer

2. Apply sanitizer (detergent and disinfectant)

3. Smooth it evenly over the hands and between the fingers, lather well, rub vigorously

4. Rinse off all lather under running water

5. Dry thoroughly

Use liquid soap preferably anti-bacterial (bacteria grows in bars of soap).

All staff should ensure that all wounds or moist skin conditions are covered with a waterproof dressing without visible air holes. Blue plasters must be worn by those involved in food preparation.

Protective Clothing

Disposable gloves must be used when dealing with any bodily fluid, infectious or contaminated waste. Gloves and aprons must be used when cleaning excreta from carpets or when using caustic agents. Staff must dispose of used aprons and gloves with the clinical waste immediately after use. Under no circumstances should staff be seen commuting to any other part of the home wearing these items. Routine bathing of residents or tending to clients personal hygiene does not warrant the routine use of gloves and aprons.

Explain to the client why you are using protective clothing as to protect both parties from cross infection.

Procedure

Wash hands thoroughly before putting on aprons and gloves. After tending to each resident the gloves and apron must be disposed of in a white bag which should be tied up and put in the yellow clinical waste bag.

Soiled Incontinent Pads, Infectious or Contaminated Waste

All excreta, dressings, etc., are to be put into white bags, tied up securely and then put outside in the yellow bags. Yellow bags - indicate clinical waste only. When 75% full the yellow bag is to be tied, labelled with the Home's address and left in appropriate place in the designated bin for collection by contractor.

Disposal of Sharps

1.   All broken crockery, glasses, etc., should be wrapped in newspaper securely and disposed of with the domestic waste.

2. Needles must be disposed of in the sharp box container. These will be collected by contractor as and when required.

Last offices. See Procedure for Death.

Soiled Linen/Clothes

1. Unless linen or clothes are soiled it is not necessary to take any special precautions and can be washed communally in warm water.

2. Excreta should be removed from linen.

3. When transporting all soiled items disposable gloves should be worn, all soiled items should be taken immediately to the laundry room in a red bag which can also be placed in the machine which will dissolve then be put on a sluice cycle first.

4. Then Hot wash – 60°C.

Infectious Residents

Diarrhoea and Vomiting

This is common in elderly persons and does not always have an infectious origin, but must be dealt with as potential infectious waste.

1. Notify G.P. If infection is suspected, he will arrange for samples of faeces to be sent to laboratory.

2. If more than two cases are suspected or known, the Consultant in Communicable Disease Control (CCDC) should be notified.

3. Residents who are vomiting should ideally be kept in a single room as long as symptoms persist. Most acute diarrhoeal infection is caused by viruses and is short-lived. These viruses are airborne and can spread rapidly. However in a bacterial infection the diarrhoea may be persistent and is not necessary to keep the resident isolated.

4. Residents, if possible, should have sole use of a designated toilet or commode as long as symptoms persist.

MRSA - Methicillin Resistant Staphylococcus Aureus

Residents who have MRSA do not present a risk to others. Eighty per cent are carriers and do not develop infection. However, any wound should be swabbed by a District Nurse and sent to the laboratory for analysis. All wounds should be treated as infectious.

When there is no wound, no special precautions need to be taken. Simple good hygiene and hand-washing is sufficient.

Blood Borne Infections

1. Residents with sudden onset of jaundice should be isolated and use a separate toilet until Hepatitis has been ruled out.

2. Residents with jaundice due to Hep B or C or those who are carriers of the virus or HIV Infection do not need isolation.

3. Laundry to be treated as infectious.

Respiratory Infections

1. Common in elderly or debilitated people. Many may be airborne, so if residents are coughing it is advisable that they stay in their room.

2. Notify GP - send sputum to the laboratory if requested by GP

3. Pneumonia is not infectious unless associated with viral influenza.

However the resident will most likely be very ill and wish to remain in their room.

Skin Infections/Infestations

1. Residents must be treated with tact and confidentiality respected.

2. Disposable gloves must be worn when cleaning any open wounds and disposed of with soiled dressing immediately. A clean pair of gloves must be used to apply topical creams.

3. Follow hand-washing procedure. Gloves must be worn to apply ointments etc., and disposed of immediately after tending to each client.

Disposal of Sanitary Ware

All ladies are reminded to use the provided sanitary bins located in the staff toilet.

Guidelines on the Control of MRSA in the Community

Overview of a report of a combined Working Party of the British Society for Antimicrobial Chemotherapy and the Hospital Infection Society (1)

The Working Party

Member of the Working Party were all national experts in the field of infection control, particularly in issues relating to MRSA and especially in the community setting. They included Consultant Microbiologists, a Community Infection Control Nurse, Consultants in Communicable Disease Control and a Nursing Home Inspection Officer.

The Need for Guidelines

The Working Party had produced two previous sets of Guidelines for the control of MRSA in hospitals (2,3). It is well recognised that issues facing those concerned with infection control in community settings are very different to those in hospitals. So, although there had been concern recently within hospitals about MRSA, it was unclear what the risks, if any, were to people in the community. It was clear however, that a rigid application of the Hospital Guidelines to the community setting was inappropriate.

Infection Control Precautions in Nursing and Residential Homes for Control of MRSA in the Community

1. It is emphasised the basic principles of infection control should be followed in all homes at all times, whether or not MRSA or other infections are known to be present.

2. Good basic hygiene and infection control measures should be routine good practices.

3. When a person is colonized with MRSA is discharged to a nursing or residential home, different arrangements may apply depending on the nature of the home to which the colonized person is to be discharged:

a. residential care where residents have intact skin, are generally healthy and receiving mainly social care - no special arrangements are necessary.

b. Residential care where some residents have pressure sores, ulcers or indwelling catheters - simple hygiene measures and nursing care should prevent spread. Basic infection control measures should be followed.

c. Residential care where residents have open post-operative wounds - basic infection control precautions should be in place plus additional measures depending on the nature of the residents conditions as advised by local infection control teams.

4. Open communication between hospitals and residential/nursing homes should be maintained. Information about residents' MRSA status should be given on transfer between hospital and community and vice versa.

5. Infection control advice may be obtained from hospital infection control teams, and Consultants in Communicable Disease Control (CsCDC) and their teams.

Conclusions

1. Colonization with MRSA should not prevent discharge from hospitals to nursing and residential homes.

2. Basic infection control principles and procedures should be routine practice.

3. Good communication between the community and hospitals is essential.

4. Should be reported to Inspection Unit and the Environmental Health.

Chapter 46

HIV And Aids Policy

Acquired Immune Deficiency Syndrome (AIDS)

AIDS is a disease that renders the body's immune system unable to resist invasion by several micro-organisms that cause serious infections. It is usually characterised by severe weight loss and fatigue, and frequently by neurological complications due to damage of cells of the brain. There is also a high incidence of certain cancers, especially Kaposi's sarcoma, which shows up as purple lesions on the skin, and tumours know as B-cell lymphomas.

Transmission of AIDS

AIDS is transmitted by blood and body fluids. It can be transmitted through intimate sexual contact, from infected mothers to their babies in the uterus, and perhaps through infected mother's milk. Before a reliable test for screening blood was developed, a major route of transmission was through receiving transfusions of contaminated blood - contaminated needles by intravenous drug abusers. Casual contact in general is not a risk factor for infection, and blood donors are definitely not at risk of catching the disease. The virus usually remains dormant for some time in infected T cells, and it may take up to 10 years for the symptoms to develop.

Much research centres on solving the problems of treating people who already have AIDS and those who have been infected with the virus but have not yet developed the syndrome. The fist chemical shown to be partially effective in reducing clinical symptoms and controlling viral replication, zidovudine, formerly called azidothymidine (AZT), was developed in 1986-87. The fatality rate from AIDS indicates that few, if any, individuals with AIDS are likely to survive in the long run, until some adequate treatment is developed.

HIV (Human Immunodeficiency Virus)
HIV can develop into AIDS but a person who is HIV positive does not mean he or she has AIDS.

All staff are encouraged to maintain their immunisations e.g. Hepatitis, polio etc. If a person suspects they have been infected. They must refrain from work and notify their GP and Environmental Health Department.

Spillage of Body Fluids

Floor and Furniture

Spillage of body fluids on the floor must be cleaned with detergent and disinfectant and gloves worn.

Body Fluids on Residents

EG. urine, faces, blood, sputum, vomit, discharge from orifices (rectum, vagina, ear, penis, wounds)

1. All body fluids must be treated as potentially infectious e.g. HIV, hepatitis, or a diagnosed infection or on a doctor's instruction for barrier nursing, persistent diarrhea, the staff must:-

a) wear disposable gloves and apron, mask if airborne, which must be disposed of with contaminated waste. (The reasons for this procedure should be explained to the resident before any care is given)

This helps to prevent direct and indirect cross-infection.

2. Where body fluid is coming from the resident who do not have any of the above infections the staff must:-

a) always wear gloves, aprons or masks, because there is a danger of infection, gloves, aprons etc. must be put on outside the area where you are to tend to the client. Supplies must be kept in all the toilets and bedrooms of where you know a client to be regularly incontinent. No member of staff should be seen wearing protective clothing around the home. These must be disposed of after every use with the clinical waste

The residents are in a residential home which is their home and therefore must be treated as such, therefore tactful use of protective clothing paramount.

Staff are advised not to have direct contact with the body fluids and always to wash their hands before and after attending to the resident.

Residents must be treated as individuals and the care provided in private. Staff are to carry out a risk assessment of each resident and to take necessary precaution when administering care.

Infectious Diseases and The Vulnerability of Elderly People

Infectious diseases are a large and important group of conditions and until recently were a major course of illness and death.

Four areas in which improvements have greatly reduced infectious dieses are:

1) Better methods for controlling the spread of diseases organisms including sanitation improved housing, pest control etc.

2) Antibiotics – since their introduction infections have greatly decreased.

3) Vaccines, which provide immunity to certain diseases.

4) Better general health and nutrition have bolstered immunity and improved survival

In developed countries a dramatic decline in poliomyelitis, diphtheria and tuberculosis has been recognized although it now seems TB is on the increased again in the UK.

This may be due to people not immunizing because they feel TB is a disease of the past it also depends on the individual factors e.g. someone whose general health is poor and persons who have immune deficiency disordered are most vulnerable or people living in unhealthy conditions.

If a resident is known or suspected to have an infectious disease the doctors and Environmental

Health Department must be notified within 24 hours.

A Regulation 37 form must be completed and sent to CSCI within 24 hours.

Clients must be cared for in a room of their own. Where they solely have access to toilet facilities. If an airborne infectious disease is suspected staff must wear disposable masks.

Chapter 47

METHODS TO BE ADMINISTERED DURING INTERVIEW

There are many styles or methods which can be administered at an interview.

Types of Interview

➢ Selection

➢ Appraisal

➢ Discipline

➢ Promotion

➢ Coaching (informal type of appraisal)

➢ Grievance

➢ Exit (when person has given in their notice to leave)

➢ Research

➢ Induction (after staff appointed)

➢ Sales

➢ Counselling

An interview involves one-to-one or one person being questioned by a panel.

Skills of Interviewer

The interviewer should have the following qualities:

(a) Questioning skills

(b) Observation skills

(c) Must be a good listener

(d) Ability to make the person being interviewed relax

(e) Ask appropriate questions

(f) Use body language – avoid jargon words

(g) Use para language e.g.

The interviewer should first read the job application and the person's CV. Ensure that there are no distractions during the interview process e.g. arrange for telephone to be diverted from the room – the room must be warm and quiet. Maintain eye contact – do not pass judgement until after the interview.

Aim

There are main questions one will need answers to: -

1. Could he/she do the job?

2. Would he/she do it and get job satisfaction?

3. Would he/she fit into the team?

4. Could his/her domestic or social life affect his/her job?

5.   Is the person qualified?

The above points are very important in the selection process.

Kinds of Questions

1.Closed questions: the answer demands a YES or NO.

2.Open questions: to encourage the person to talk more e.g. tell me... have you

Always encourage the person to talk more. Avoid leading questions. Try to control the flow of the interview.

Technique

Always begin each section with closed questions, followed by open questions. The probing questions (e.g. why did you ....? Then back to closed questions). Then summaries before moving to the next question.

First read the application form and CV. The interview starts from the moment the applicant rings the doorbell. Welcome him/her, give them a seat and give them an application form to complete (if it has not already been completed).

An interview involves observation. Using the five senses, observe:

(a)   how the person is dressed

(b)   How he/she walks

(c)   How he/she speaks

(d)   How he/she answers questions in a relaxed and pressurized atmosphere

(e)   Observe personality, honesty, assess his/her experience

At the end of the interview, invite any questions from the applicant and give honest answers. If you feel the applicant is suitable, you or a senior member of the staff should show the person around the home.

Conclude by thanking him/her and assure them that they will be contacted after relevant references have been taken.

Chapter 48

INTRUDERS

DEFINITION: a person coming to the home (within the grounds or building) without consent by staff or residents.

Research: police inspector, neighbourhood watch, legal adviser

1)   dial 999 immediately (i.e. if you see an intruder outside. if intruder is inside the staff who is not talking to the intruder should phone the police immediately - if possible phone the person on call)

the person who sees the intruder inside the home should:

shout loudly or scream in order to attract attention of the other staff.

The other staff seeing the colleague with the intruder should run and set off the fire alarm by breaking the fire alarm and if possible set off the nurse call system.

(c) The intruder might run away thinking the alarm is security.

(d) The entrance door left open.

(e) Dial 999. Inform police of intruder. If unable to speak Dial 999 and leave the phone off the hook and the police will be able to trace the address.

(f) If the phone is cut by the intruder the free staff should set off the fire alarm, run out of the Home and ask a neighbour to call the police and help.

(g) The free staff should then return to the Home immediately to help take care of the residents.

2) The staff with the intruder must talk to him/her

3) Remain calm

4) One member of staff to ensure residents are alright

5) Ask what the intruder wants

6) Ask intruder to leave but don't force intruder out

7) Observe and if possible take description of the intruder, physical and mental state, note any special features (refer to details in the missing persons file)

8) Record description and inform person on call

9) Find out how the person entered the home

10) note any damage caused or goods stolen and record

11) Do not confront or attack the intruder

12) If the intruder is outside do not let them in the home unless you or others are at risk of harm.

13) If the intruder tries to take anything or demands anything, do not put yourself or others at risk. give the

261

intruder what he wants and make a record of it.

14) staff will complete a full house check at 8 pm and also at 11 pm. this is to be documented in the security check book. any open windows at 8 pm must be communicated to the night staff during handover.

after the incident prepare a written report for the manager and the national care standards commission.

all incidents must be reported to the csci as per regulation 37

Chapter 49

PROCEDURE FOR LOSS OF MAINS

gas, water and electricity

GAS LEAK OR LOSS

A gas leak can be recognised by a smell of gas in the area.

Loss of gas is recognised by the loss of use of gas equipment e.g. gas cooker.

If you smell a gas leak:-

1. Turn off the gas at the mains.

This will avoid or reduce the risk of an explosion.

2. Phone the Gas Board emergency number (in Croydon the number is 020-88684 6666 or telephone Directory Enquiries 192 for gas emergency number).

3. Give the Gas Board details of the premises including the address, telephone number, type of business, the location of the meter and the name of the person reporting the problem.

4. Open all the windows and doors for ventilation.

5. Do not switch on or off any electrical appliances or switches. Do not use the lift. This is to avoid a spark which can ignite and cause an explosion.

All residents and staff must not go back to the area where the gas is suspected to be leaking from until the Gas Board have been and confirm that it is safe to go back.

Make a statement of events in the Incident Book.

WATER (LOSS OR FLOODING)

Loss of water means there is no water to the property at all.

Flooding is as a result of an sink overflow or blocked/burst pipe.

WHAT TO DO IN THE EVENT OF LOSS OF WATER

1. Contact the emergency telephone number of the Water Board (in Croydon the number is 0645 200800) immediately.

2. Give your name, address and telephone number of the property, the type of business and the people who live in the property.

3. The Water Board will advise you if there is any work being carried out in the area or if

there is an emergency such as a burst main or property flooding.

4. You may be requested to check with your neighbours to make sure that you are not the only one in the area.

5. Explain the situation to the residents and assure them that you are dealing with the matter.

6. The Water Board engineer or technician will come as soon as possible.

PLANNED REPAIRS BY WATER BOARD (LOSS OF WATER

Usually the customer (the Home) is informed in advance of planned repairs and the date, time and duration of the work. The staff must readjust the routine to ensure that a routine that requires use of water is done before the water is cut off (e.g. bathing, washing, washing up).

All the residents should have a full jug of water in their bedrooms (for drinking). Fill all the baths with water so that it can be used to clean the resident.

Fill as many saucepans as possible with water and store them in the kitchen or the refrigerator.

Be more economical with the use of the water without putting the residents in danger.

PS   after the mains is cut off there will still be water in the house from the cold-water tank usually in the loft.

FLOODING

1.   If the flooding is near the main electric or gas meters then turn them off immediately.

2.   Telephone the Water Board emergency number immediately (Croydon: 0645 200800) who will send a technician.

3.   Turn off the internal stop valve (stop cock).

4.   If that fails you can turn off the external stop valve (stop cock) usually located on the footpath of the road.

5.   Assess the severity of the flooding in relation to the safety of the residents. Call the on-call staff member who can arrange for more staff to assist.

6.   You may need to move residents to a safe area e.g. upstairs or telephone the fire brigade and ambulance service for assistance.

When emergency situation is over make a record of what took place in the Incident Book.

ELECTRICITY (LOSS OF)

In case of loss of electricity:-

1. Check the fuse and circuit breaker.

2. If they are all in order then telephone the emergency number for the electricity engineer (0345 222222). The Home is registered as a priority customer so they will come as soon as possible.

3. Do not panic because the emergency lighting will come on automatically in case of loss of mains of electricity.

4. Check the property internally, if you smell any burning turn the main electric meter off immediately.

5. Explain the situation to the residents and assure them that you are dealing with the situation.

When the problem is resolved make a statement in the Incident Book.

Chapter 50

JOB DESCRIPTION: MANAGER

Name:

Role: Registered Manager in Residential Home

Title: Manager

Responsible to: Director/The Proprietors and the Care Standards Commission Inspectorate

Report to: The General Manager and Proprietor/Director, CSCI Inspectors

Minimum

Qualification: Two years' experience as Senior Carer in Residential Home plus four excellent references plus clearance of medical. DBS clearance and working towards or to have NVQ Level 4 in Care and RMA award (or their equivalent).

AIM OF POST To have completed all mandatory courses as stated by C.S.C.I

To implement approved care policy in the Home and to co-ordinate the work of the senior, ancillary and junior staff. To confer with the multi-disciplinary team on the general care of the Residents. To adhere to the aims and objectives of the home and statement of purpose.

KEY TASKS

1. Organise and maintain an efficient care service throughout the Home day and night in accordance with the National Care Standards and the Home's policy and aims and objectives. Inform the proprietor of the implications of the implications of the policy and any difficulties in the implementation of such policy and aims/objectives.

2. Maintain personal contact with the community and Residents and their relatives, by acting as the representative of the Home.

3. Maintenance of a high standard of Resident's care in the Home and of channels of communications which ensure that these standards are known and applied.

FUNCTION

To be responsible for all care staff.

1. Interview - taking references - employ and dismiss staff according to the policy of the Home. Keep satisfactory records of all staff employed, including supervision at least 6 times a year and an annual appraisal.

2. Instructing or supervising staff as per their job description e.g. on matters effecting welfare of the Residents and the Home. Observing the requirements of the CSCI Standards.

3. Maintain records and rendering returns as required to a high standard as required by the Proprietor and the CSCI.

4. Participating in meal service for Residents, nutritional needs of residents, supervision of special diets and adjusting nutritional needs, enlisting such experts in such nutritional needs as necessary.

5. Maintaining Home stores, equipment and ensuring for provisions, repairs and replacements as required.

6.   Instigating emergency repairs on their initiative and advising the proprietor of such circumstances.

COMMUNICATION AND LIAISON

1.   Promote and maintain overall system of communication. Be responsible for liaising, where, necessary, with community e.g. Residents' relatives, Chaplains, GP, OT, social worker, pharmacy, physiotherapist, transport, visitors, welfare associations, religious and voluntary organisations, official visitors as required. Attend staff meetings once a month or when required.

Instigating references for such persons coming into the Home as voluntary workers.

2.   Preparing, receiving and giving reports as required.

3.   Instigating care plans and liaising with staff to implement such care plans efficiently.

FIRE

Ensure that all grades of staff are familiar with fire prevention precautions and have received proper instructions e.g. that staff are aware of the action they should take in the event of a fire. Ensure that all fire exits are kept clear and fire notices are permanently and prominently displayed at all times.

EDUCATION

1. Participate in the "In-Service" training and Induction Programme for staff.
2. Inform the proprietor of any special training needs.
3. Use the record of instructions and the Health and Safety at work.
4. Develop management skills of your senior staff.
5. To keep up to date with relevant legislation.
6. The Manager must ensure that they keep up to date with training and complete mandatory courses.

STAFFING

Try to keep staff ratio as per latest legislation guidelines.

ADMINISTRATIVE

If a Proprietor stands in to work in the Home in the absence of the Manager, the Proprietor will act as Manager. If the Proprietor works in the home whilst the Manager is on duty the Proprietor must be treated as a Senior Care Assistant.

COMMUNICATION

Do not hesitate to discuss anything you wish with the Proprietor - who is available at all times over 24-hour x 7 days a week period.

INFORMATION

STOCKTAKING

Monthly check to be done by day or night staff.

REFERENCES OF PROSPECTIVE RESIDENTS

Assess by Manager and discuss and agree with the Proprietor before admission, if on a border line Manager must discuss with Proprietor and CSCI. Consideration must be given to Residents already in the Home. Prospective residents must be assessed against the home's admission criteria.

MEETINGS

For the first month in-post house meetings with the Proprietor once a week. After that meetings to be held once a fortnight for 3 months, then 3 monthly. Arrange regular meetings within Home of all the staff i.e. Manager, senior and junior care assistants. Residents meetings not less than 3 monthly.

EMPLOYING STAFF

Organise staff rota to ensure satisfactory cover at all times. Do not employ friends, relatives of staff or residents. The Manager must ensure adequate experienced and trained staff who can meet the client's needs. All staff employed must meet the CSCI requirements and current legislation.

ROUTINES

Ensure that daily, weekly routines are implemented except in an emergency.

FINANCE

To ensure all residents are in receipt of personal allowance and that this is recorded

Ensure all residents contracts are signed and updated annually

 Ensure all care fees are paid and recorded.

Chase up overdue fees.

PERSONNEL

1. Exercising leadership by personal example and maintaining morale of care staff in the Home.

2. Taking all possible steps to safeguard the health, welfare and safety of staff and residents.

3. Introducing new members of staff to their duties and orientating them to the structure and the Home's geography.

4. Control and direct staff by good leadership.

5. Counselling, advising and supporting staff as required.

MAINTENANCE OF HIGH STANDARDS

Monitor and inspect that work is carried out in accordance with agreed policy and that a satisfactory service is provided and maintained.

Informing the Proprietor where appropriate of accidents or complaints in the Home and assisting in investigating such incidents in accordance with the Home's policy.

Arranging for safe keeping of residents property, money and valuables in accordance with the Home's policy.

ENVIRONMENTAL HYGIENE

Co-operate with staff to keep the Home clean and tidy and monitor such standards as a matter of routine.

SPECIALIST FUNCTIONS

Carry out administrative tasks and fact-finding exercises as requested by the Proprietor. Do all that is possible to maintain and promote the good image of the Home.

1. List of food requirements.

2. Calculate weekly hours of staff.

3. Bring to the Proprietor or General Manager's notice any requirements of the Home.

4. Ensure staff wears decent clothes. Encouraging them to wear their own clothes as per the Home's dress code.

5. Ensure staff adheres to the Home Policies and Procedures and the Code of Conduct.

MESSAGES

Messages for Proprietor to be given straight away by phone. Efficient use of the diary, listing staff on duty AM/PM and night. All messages received to be put in the diary. All messages received to be put in the diary.

FOOD, Responsible for carrying out of procedure in the requisition and distribution of stores and equipment and maintain accurate stock control records.

SUMMARY In essence the Manager has full control of the day to day running of the Home.

Termination of Employment of a Manager is a minimum of 12 weeks. Periods of absence/leave of more than 1 month must be reported to the Proprietor well in advance.

Signature   Date

Chapter 51

MEDICATION PROCEDURES

Medicines With Care

Carers should be aware of the hazards of careless handling of drugs which may cause skin sensitivity i.e. penicillin, Chlorpromazine, or the misuse of antiseptics or disinfectant solutions.

Medicines should;

• Only be given in accordance with the doctors directions

• Be kept out of the reach of children

• Never be taken from unlabelled containers

• Never be shared with others

• Never be transferred from one container to another

• Be returned to the pharmacy when they are out of date or unused

• Never be handled. Use the lids of the containers to transfer medicines from the bottle to the person concerned

277

Procedure For Dispensing Medication From Monitored Dosage System

The keys to all medicine cupboards are to be kept on the person in charge at all times.

The times of day that the drugs are administered are colour coded and are as follows:

Pink   Morning   7.00 a.m. to 9.30 a.m.

YellowLunchtime   12.30 to 1.00 p.m.

Orange   Supper   5.30 p.m. to 6.00 p.m.

Blue   Night 9.00 p.m. to 10.00 p.m.

White Short course medication or PRN

The system is on a 28-day basis commencing on and is blister packed. Each drug is on a separate card with the person's name, drug name and dose. Divider cards separate one resident from another.

Syrups, Short Courses and PRN Medication

Any resident who is prescribed syrups, eye drops or has a short course of medication e.g. anti-biotics will have a reminder card at the time due for administration to remind staff to dispense accordingly.

PRN medication is to be administered as per procedure.

Dispensing

Medicine pots should be taken with the tray of drugs.

Check person's name corresponds with each card and dose. Check you are giving on the correct day.

Lay medicine pot under each tray and pop out drugs. Do not touch medication. See Medicines with Care.

Give to resident and sign on medication sheet immediately they have taken them.

Non -Compliance / Refusal

Clients who are non- compliant with medication must not be deceived by staff putting medication into their food etc. If a client is unwilling to take tablets alternatives may be discussed with their GP/psychiatrist re syrups or injections.

The client's GP/psychiatrist must be kept informed if non-compliance continues for maximum of 3 days.

Refused Medication or Omitted Medication If a resident refuses medication or omits for other reasons. The tablet/s should stay in pack and be recorded in medication sheet accordingly - referring to key:-

R - Refused

    S - Sleeping

    P - Pulse abnormal

    H - Hospitalised

    D - Destroyed

    N - Nausea

    L - On leave

    O - Other

Different forms of Monitored Dose System may have a different key.

If a client refuses medication try alternative ways of persuasion. Discuss with GP to change formation e.g. change tablet to liquid or ask another staff member to prompt/persuade.

If a client refuses the medication once dispensed form the blister packs, they must be put into an envelope and the drug name, dose, date, time and person's name to be written on envelope. The envelope should be put in drug return container. This is also to be entered into the Medicine Return Book and care notes. All medication that is refused must be reported to the GP.

Medication Stock

When drugs are delivered they are to be checked by two persons. The residents name, drug name and dose should correspond with medication profile. Each drug is to be checked and signed on medication sheet.

At the end of each cycle the medication which is left over will be returned to the pharmacy for disposal as well as the empty trays. All drugs to be disposed of are to be entered in Medicine Disposal Book and signed by the staff entering in the book. When the pharmacist collects the Returns he/she must sign the Drug Return Book and check it corresponds with the stock in the return box.

Discontinued Medication

When the doctor wishes to discontinue or alter the dose of a certain drug he must cross it off , date and sign the medication profile.

Staff should remove the medicine card from dosage system. Write in care notes that the doctor has been and reason for discontinuation.

Unused medication to be put in medicine cupboard in appropriate box.

Death

The Home to keep all mediation and records for seven days after death. After that medicine must be transferred to pharmacy and record kept in deceased file.

New Prescriptions Or Altered Medication

If the doctor wishes to increase or decrease the dose of a particular drug or writes up a new drug then we need a prescription. Doctor is to write on medication profile: drug name, dose and times to be given.

Staff to let resident sign back of prescription or staff to complete (if appropriate). Pharmacist will deliver medication. Check with him that the new drug corresponds with prescription. Put drugs into monitored dose system at the correct times.

PRN Medication

Ask GP to write PRN on prescription in order for the pharmacy to print on MAR sheet.

Prescription of Cream

The GP must state which part of the body the cream is to be applied to.

When Resident Comes Out Of Hospital

If Monday-Friday, ring doctors' surgery and ask for a prescription for resident's medication.

Ring pharmacist to collect prescription and ask him to bring up medication in monitored dose.

If surgery is closed or pharmacist unable to bring up drugs then staff are to use bottles from hospital until M/dose drugs are brought up.

If resident is using drugs from bottles it is vital that this information is recorded in care notes and medication sheets and passed on to staff during handover.

When monitored dose drugs arrive they are to be put into system and record in care notes and medication sheet. Bottles can now be put into box which will be returned to pharmacy.

Admission of New Resident

Doctor should be informed. If resident is to change GP then appropriate form to be completed.

Bottles of medicine to be used until the doctor has seen resident and written up prescription.

Procedure as per when resident comes out of hospital.

Self- Medicating Residents

Residents who wish to self-medicate and GP/Psychiatrist has agreed can be given the option of using bottles or monitored dosage system, whichever they prefer. The consent form to self- medicate must be signed by the doctor and resident. All medication given to the resident each month must be signed for.

Drugs initially to be checked weekly for six weeks by keyworker that the resident is taking medication correctly. Then to be checked monthly.

If the resident is depressed, suicidal or unstable then the GP or Psychiatrist is to be informed.

If resident agrees the staff may administer drugs during period of illness.

Controlled Drugs

When the pharmacist dispenses controlled drugs, staff must check the number of tablets/amounts of liquid, the name, dosage, date of dispensing and expiry date on the packaging.

When you are happy that all of the details are correct ask the pharmacist to sign in the controlled drugs book, and the member of staff who is present with the pharmacist should also witness in the controlled drugs book that all details are correct.

Controlled Drug Book

The controlled drugs book must contain:

The name of the resident

The name of the drug

The dosage of the drug

The quantity of the drug held on the premises before and after dispensing

Signature of staff dispensing/administering drug

Signature of the witness who must be present throughout procedure

Signature of change of staff witness

The time the drug is given must be recorded

Storage

Controlled drugs must be kept in a locked metal cupboard within a locked metal dry cupboard, under DDA (Dangerous Drug Act 1972).

Administration

1.There must always be two people to check the writing on the box   e.g. name, dose, time, expiry date.

2.The quantity in the bottle must correspond with the number in the book.

3.Two staff must count and agree on number counted.

4. Take medicine from the bottle or box.

5.Put the box or bottle back in the double locked cupboard

6.Both staffs are to take the medicine and controlled drugs book to the resident and both staffs to check residents name.

7.Give resident the medicine and make sure he/she swallows it.

8.Both staffs sign in the controlled drugs book - i.e. the staff who gave the drug and the staff who witnessed it.

9.Record in resident's care notes the drug name, dose and time given in red pen and sign

Staff Change Over

Senior staff going off duty must check the medicine(quantity etc.) with the staff in charge who is taking over. Both staffs should sign in the controlled drugs book to make sure and witness that the incoming staff has taken over the correct quantity of medicine.

If Quantity Is Wrong

1.   Inform officer on call.

2.   The officer will instigate internal investigation through interviewing all staff from previous duty when the quantities were up to date.

3.   The officer on call will inform the doctor.

Medication Which Falls Or Resident Spits Out

If a resident refuse and has not touched the medicine it can be returned to the container and recorded as refused   again both staffs should sign to record this.

If the tablet is contaminated   put it in an envelope with a lid, label it with name of resident, name of drug, dose, time contaminated. Record the wastage in the controlled drugs book. Take the wastage to the pharmacist who will sign the controlled drugs book and dispose of the wasted drug. Inform the doctor of any wastage and ask for another prescription.

Prescription Abbreviations

Prescriptions are written in Latin by the doctor. There meaning are as follows:-

MANE   -   MORNING

NOCTE   NIGHT

OD   -   DAILY (USUALLY MORNING UNLESS

OTHERWISE STATED)

BD   -   TWICE DAILY

TDS   -   THREE TIMES A DAY

QDS   -   FOUR TIMES A DAY

PRN   (as and when needed

•   =   1 tablet

• •   =   2 tablets

• • •   =   3 tablets

therefore - examples would be

A prescription written: Paracetamol 500 mg T.D.S. would mean:

    Paracetamol 500 mg two tablets (1 g) 3 times a day (3 g Paracetamol a day)

A prescription written: Frusemide 40mg • • daily (mane) would mean:

    Frusemide 40mg two tablets (80mg) in the morning

Injections given by CPNs and district nurses

All visits by CPN, District Nurses must be recorded in the care notes and community service sheets.

S/C - subcutaneous - (sub-cut) - an injection given just under the skin - (usually an orange needle). Drugs given S/C are Insulin, Heparin. Site of Injection: upper arms, thighs, abdomen

I/M - Intra-Muscular - (into a muscle) usually a blue needle or for larger people a green needle). Drugs given I/M are depot injections, anti-sickness, pain killers etc. Site of injection: buttocks, outer thigh

I/V - Intra-Venus - (into a vein) - usually via a drip or a needle already inset in a vein. Most drugs can be given into a vein usually to gain a faster effect.

Frequency or Fixed Period Prescription

1./7 a figure over 7 means days e.g. 5/7 would be a course for 5 days (i.e., 7 (seven) days in a week)

2./52 a figure over 52 means weeks e.g. 2/52 would be every two weeks (i.e., 52 (fifty-two) weeks in a year)

3. /12 a figure over 12 means months e.g. 1/12 would be every month (i.e., 12 months in a year)

Training

All staff who deal with medication must:

• attend training

• read the Home's policy

• read Skills for Care "Knowledge Set for Medication" , "Knowledge Set for Progress Log" – copies obtained from the Office or Skills for Care website (www.skillsforcare.org.uk).

Care And Use Of Drugs

Storage Of Drugs

In a Residential home medicines should be stored in a medicine cupboard, lockable and fixed to the wall in a safe, cool and dry environment, like the office. The key to this cupboard must always be with the staff in charge.

Self- Administration

Medicines must be kept in a personal lockable drawer or cupboard and the key kept on the person.

Before a decision is made for self-administration the manager must:

Risk assess the resident. Ascertain if it is the choice of the resident. With the residents knowledge discuss with the next of kin and general practitioner. Complete Risk Assessment form, evaluate as per assessment indicated.

If you get the support of the general practitioner and the manager agrees then the resident can self-administered. The risk assessment form must be countersigned by the client and the CP or psychiatrist.

The manager must make sure that regular checks are made to ensure that residents are taking prescribed medication, that they are safely stored and locked away, and that the resident has a sufficient supply. Failure to do this could result in medicines lying around, residents taking medication that is out of date, lack of medication.

Self-Administered Insulin

If insulin is drawn up by a district nurse, the morning and evening syringes must be stored in separate boxes in a fridge. Before the syringe is given to the client it must be checked by two staff authorized to dispense medication and by the client themselves.

Refusal

If a client refuses medication the staff must discreetly ask the client the reason for this refusal. The member of staff must then fully explain the reason for that particular prescribed drug(s) (see Mediation Profile) and the consequences which may occur if the medication is not taken. If the prescribed medication is for diabetes, epilepsy, heart condition or any other serious illness, which would be detrimental to the client if not taken, the staff must inform the GP and person on-call. The member of staff should approach the client up to an hour later to retry. A record of all refused incidences must be made in the client's care notes and on the MAR sheet. If this is recurrent i.e. more than 3 times (irrespective of why the drug is prescribed) it must be discussed with the GP/Psychiatrist.

Medication Which Falls Or Resident Spits Out

If a resident refuse and has not touched the medicine it can be returned to the container and recorded as refused again both staffs should sign to record this.

If the tablet is contaminated put it in an envelope with a lid, label it with name of resident, name of drug, dose, time contaminated. Record the wastage on the MAR sheet and the Medicine To Return To Pharmacy book.

Staff Administration Of Drugs

Make sure the resident has swallowed the medication before leaving him/her. One can do this by either asking the resident if it has been swallowed, or asking if they do not wish to take it.(This will avoid medication being left lying around)

Do not sign for the medication until you are positive that the medicine has been taken. If medication is refused this should be indicated on the medication card and in the care notes. It may help to know the reason why the resident does not want to take the medication.

Staff should know why the resident is taking the medication and know the reason why the drug administered was prescribed

Staff should be aware of and observe for any side effects or allergic reactions to medication.

Common Side Effects

these include

1. mental confusion almost any drug but especially digoxin, diuretics, diuretics, propranolol.

2. constipation e.g. codeine, iron, tranquilisers, orphenadrine, co hydromel, nifedipine, verapamil, benzhexol, amitriptyline.

3. diarrhoea

   e.g. antibiotic, magnesium mixtures.

4. falls and giddiness

   tranquilisers, diuretics.

5. drowsiness, unsteady, gait, slurred speech

   hypnotics, antihistamines, temazepam.

6. indigestion

   e.g. aspirin, ibuprofen.

7. parkinsons

   tranquilisers, stemetil.

8. dry mouth, blurred vision, urinary retention

   antidepressants.

9. skin disorders

   photosensitivity, diuretics, Librium.

10. aggression, hostility

    benzodiazepines.

precautions

a Never transfer medicine from original container to another

b; never mix tablets   could be different tablets or dosage

c do not give if colour or appearance alters

d. never give medicine prescribed for someone else

e. always check expiry dates

f. when in doubt do not give

if there is suspicion of an overdose treat the resident as an emergency i.e. dial 999

follow the procedure for dealing with overdose and poison.

P.R.N drugs (i.e. drugs to be taken when needed)

To avoid some staff misusing P.R.N. drugs and residents having unnecessary medication.   PRN medication needs to be written up correctly.

P.R.N. medication: It is the responsibility of senior staff to carry out observation, effect of the drug on the resident and to report to the G.P. to review the medication if required. It helps with G.P. being called unnecessarily.

All prescribed P.R.N. medication has to state on the medication profile and MAR sheet.

a)   Name

b)   Dose

c)   Amount

d)   Strength

e)   Number to be taken at specific interval within 24 hours.

f)   The specific reason why the drug is prescribed.

g)   Under what circumstances the drug is to be given.

Staff must ensure these instructions and documented before admitting any PRN Medication.

All prescriptions on medicine bottle must agree with what is written on the medicine profile. It confirms that the pharmacy has witnessed what the doctors have prescribed. The staff are then fully protected.

Note: Staff should be aware of the signs and symptoms for which the P.R.N. medication is prescribed, and it should not be given for any other reason, other than what the medication has been prescribed this for.

Not Acceptable: The following methods of prescription are not acceptable to the home management. Examples:

1)   Haloperidol 50mg P.R.N.

2)   Haloperidol to be taken as directed (direction should be put on the prescription.

This does not state the intervals between doses, how many tablets or under circumstances the drug should be given.

All P.R.N. (as any other drugs) must be signed for on the medicine profile. If the P.R.N. drug is given, then when it is given it should be written in the care note. If P.R.N. is given for three days consecutively, the doctor should be notified.

Obtain the doctor's signature on the medicine profile when P.R.N. is prescribed and cancelled.

Household Remedies

All household remedies are agreed by the Homes GP. Staff must follow the instructions given in the household remedy book.

The choice, independence and integrity of the residents must be respected. The residents (if he has mental faculty intact) or next of kin or friends could legally bring household remedies to the Home but they should follow and respect the policy of the Home, since the Home will take partial responsibility for the effect of the medicine.

Policy On Household Remedies

All residents should be advised to discuss, with the staff in charge, any household remedies they may have or propose to have in the Home.

All visitors (friends, next of kin, etc.) should discuss with the staff in charge before any medication or alcohol is given to the resident.

One of the main reasons is that the resident may be on medication which may not be compatible or could result in neutralising the prescribed medication or could result in an overdose of the chemical in the medicine.

The staff in charge must discuss with the pharmacy or GP if he or she is not sure of the effect of the household remedies in relation to the resident's diagnosis or prescribed medication.

The staff must keep records of household medication and how often the residents take them. Obtain the signature of the next of kin or residents who bought the medicine.

Also make note if this has been discussed with the GP or pharmacy and their comment.

For about one month, carry out unobtrusive observation on the resident for any unusual behaviour or side effect. If there is any side effect, advise resident to stop taking the medicine and inform the GP.

Residents who may be capable of managing their own drugs but may appear depressed or unwell must not be allowed to dispense their own drugs. If in doubt discuss with the G.P. or registration authority. When the resident does recover from his/her depression or suicidal state the resident could assume his/her self-administration of drugs (if in doubt discuss with G.P.).

A monthly stock take is carried out on the 1st of each month by a designated person. All household remedies must be recorded in the Household Remedy Book and the care notes. Check the person can have the drug first. If after 3 doses of a household remedy the staff must notify the GP.

Chapter 52

POLICY FOR MEETINGS

The manager and proprietor - The manager and proprietor have a regular monthly meeting.

Staff meetings

Manager and all staff - There is a monthly meeting for all staff on the 1st day of each month at 1pm.

Residents Meetings

Resident meetings – held every 3 months – residents have the opportunity to meet individuals with their keyworker every month for a key working session and a monthly meeting with the manager.

In an emergency a meeting can be called at any time e.g. if the proprietor/manager wants information to be passed on immediately.

Chapter 53

PROCEDURE FOR MISSING PERSONS FROM THE HOME

By Missing Person we mean a resident who (in the judgement of the home) is a danger to him/herself or to the public, who has left the home without informing the staff or fails to return two hours after expected arriving time and having had no contact from either the resident or the person the resident is visiting. See individual client's risk assessment for agreed times to report client's missing.

On discovering resident missing:

a)   Inform the other staff.

b)   Ask fellow residents if they have seen missing person.

c)   One staff search the Home, and another search the grounds or gardens. Go outside the front and back gate and look to see if you can see resident walking. If not go back to the Home. (Do not get into car to search for resident).

d)   If the resident is not found within a reasonable time, contact local relatives and friends to establish whether the resident has been visiting them. If this fails, notify the police giving them the information they require. NB. Tell them straight away if the missing person is depressed, suicidal, on special medical or very confused. This will enable the police to treat the case as a priority.

e) Complete the missing persons form before the police arrive for details.

f) Inform Manager or on call staff after discovering resident missing and also once found.

g) If the resident does not return within 2 hours of expected time of return, inform the Social Services Care Manager and The National Care Standards Commission.

h) When resident is found, assess his/her physical and mental state and give necessary care. Obtain a statement from the resident confirming who found him/her. Contact all those who were informed that the resident was missing and inform them of his/her return.

i)   Make him/her comfortable.

k)   Make notes in the care notes.

l)   The Manager will use his/her discretion when to inform the doctor.

m)   The Senior Keyworker must bring the case of a resident who persistently goes missing to the care team for review of the resident's care, in the Home

Chapter 54

NOTIFICATION OF DEATH, ILLNESS, ACCIDENT OR INCIDENT

Regulation 37

1. The person registered shall notify the CSCI, not later than 24 hours from the time of its occurrence and the placing authority should also be informed if a resident is involved:

a) of the death of any resident and of the circumstances of his death;

b) of the outbreak in the home of any infectious disease which in the opinion of any Registered Medical Practitioner attending persons in the home is sufficiently serious to be so notified, or of any serious injury to or serious illness of any person residing in the home;

c) of any unexplained absence of a resident from the home;

d) of any event in the home which affects the well-being of any resident;

e) of any theft, accident, burglary, fire or accident in the home.

f) of any allegations of misconduct by the manager or staff.

All forms must be sent to: CSCI or CQC

Chapter 55

Nutritional Risk Assessment

The need for nutritional assessment

The National Minimum Standards and Care Homes regulations require Homes to assess the needs of the service users. Standard 3.1 states that: -

New service users are admitted only on top of the basis of a full assessment undertaken by the people who are trained to do so, and to which the prospective service user, his/her representatives (if any) and relevant professionals have been party. While standard 3.3 details the areas that such an assessment must cover and clearly states that it includes diet and weight, including dietary preferences

It is therefore necessary to use a simple screening tool to identify the nutritional risk of the service users, both existing and new. From this information it is then possible to ensure that their nutritional needs are met.

How to assess the nutritional risk

The screening tool has been developed by the Community Dietician for Southern Derbyshire Health Authority and is an adapted version of the one used in hospitals. The Manager using information from the Service User their family and/or carers must complete the assessment, which is in two parts.

Part 1 – records general information about the service users, their eating patterns, likes, dislikes and other dietary information.

Part 2 – requires more detail that allows the manager to identify the nutritional risk category for each service user i.e. high, medium or low.

Action following the assessment

Having identified the nutritional risk of each service user the 'Nutritional Guidance Risk Chart' outlines the most appropriate course of action.

An important part of the assessment process is to record the weight of each service user. It is the best to weigh an individual dressed and with their shoes on at approximately the same time of day on the same scales to ensure the accuracy of the measurement. This information must be recorded on the 'Weight Recording Chart'.

Service users who are found to be in the high and medium risk categories need to have their food intake monitored for 3 days. This needs to be a very accurate record of the food that's an individual consumes rather than is offered. Therefore it must be very specific i.e. ½ slice of white bread, teaspoon of jam, ¼ cup of tea. This information needs to be recorded on the Food intake chart.

If it necessary for a doctor or a dietician to visit a resident because there is concern for their nutritional risk, copies of the following must be made available to them: -

- Nutritional Assessment Forms
- Weight Record Chart
- Food Intake Charts

It is advisable the assessment, weight recording chart and any food intake charts in a specified place e.g. as part of the residents care file or a separate 'Nutrition' file.

Chapter 56

PETS

No pets unless it is agreed in writing with the Management/ Proprietor and then only if the pet does not constitute any risk of injury or infection/ill health to the Residents and Staff at the Home. All costs incurred by such pets will be borne by the Resident (e.g. veterinary fees, feeding, etc.). Please note that the only pets that would be allowed into residents' rooms are birds and fish.

Chapter 57

POLICIES AND PROCEDURES REVIEW

The content of our policies and forms used are reviewed yearly in April and when necessary.

When we review our policies, the Home tries to be open-minded and receptive to all proposals and suggestions, therefore we take into account :

1. Views expressed during staff meetings.
2. expressed during resident meetings and keyworker sessions.
3. Our Inspector's knowledge and experience, which is normally discussed during annual inspections, ad-hoc visits or advice being sort by the Manager.
4. Views and suggestions from residents, next of kin, staff, visitors, Social Services, the Inspectors from the CSCI, Care Managers, Environmental and Fire Safety Departments etc
5. Regular bulletins or information received from the Social Services, Department of Health and Social Security, the Health Authorities, The National Care Standards Commission

6. Information received from other people's mistakes and accidents within the local Borough and other Boroughs. Such information can be obtained from reading The Social Care Magazines and also our proprietor has other Homes in other Boroughs.

7. Relevant legislation relating to care homes. All policies/procedures will be amended as and when legislation changes.

Chapter 58

PRESSURE RELEIF

All clients whose mobility is limited or who has poor circulatory problems will be assessed by the District Nurse for pressure relieving aids, their advice will be added to the Care Plan. The Home must identify the risk by completing a Risk Assessment Form.

The Home will use the aids loaned by The Health Authority as per their instructions. The advice of the GP or Dietician will be sought for their advice on diet (usually a high protein diet is recommended).

Staff will ensure that as per the individual clients care plan, the care given will be aimed as prevention of pressure sores. All red areas or wounds will be reported to the GP. No wounds will be dressed by our care staff. The skills of the District Nurse will be sought.

Chapter 59

PROMOTING CONTINENCE

It is the Home's policy that if a resident becomes incontinent or experiences changes to their usual urinary or bowel habits the GP will be notified. If after his/her assessment they feel the problem is of a long-term nature or requires further investigations the client will be referred to a urologist (if the resident is experiencing urinary problems) a general surgeon or gastroenterologist if the client is experiencing bowel changes. Or the advice of a continence advisor may be sought. No client should use incontinent aids without the advice of a professional person who specializes in this field.

Incontinence

There may be many causes of incontinence. Each cause and the particular needs of the client may be remedied with a different approach so it is imperative that staff follow the individual care plan of each client, some causes may be:

a) prostate enlargement in men exhibiting in frequency, urgency and dribbling of urine.

b) Neurological damage e.g. strokes

c) Urinary tract infection or cystitis; common symptoms include an offensive odor, dark amber in colour, pain on passing urine and frequency

d) Dementia

e) Some medication increases urine output e.g. diuretics (water tablets) or laxatives may cause urgency to empty bowels.

f) Psychological e.g. depression, unmotivated, attention seeking.

g) Faecal impaction causing leaking from the rectum.

If a client requires a toileting programmed (should be agreed with continence advisor) the toileting procedure should be followed.

CHAPTER 60

PSYCHOTIC EXPERIENCES

- Each individual's experiences are unique.

  Many people who have psychotic experiences do not come into contact with mental health services because they do not find their experiences distressing. Some people, however, are so distressed by them that they seek professional help or others seek help on their behalf.

- Psychotic experiences include hearing voices (sometimes called 'hallucinations') holding beliefs that other people find unusual or hard to understand (sometimes called delusions) and experiencing strong fluctuations in mood.

- About one person in one hundred is likely to receive a diagnosis of schizophrenia in their lifetime, and similarly about one person in one hundred is likely to receive a diagnosis of bipolar disorder (manic depression).

- Between 100,000 and 500,000 people in the UK today are likely to have been given the diagnosis of schizophrenia, and about 500,000 are likely to have received a diagnosis of bipolar disorder (manic depression).

- Social circumstances are very important. People from disadvantaged backgrounds, especially young men, seem at greatest risk of receiving a diagnosis of schizophrenia. However, although the risks might vary, almost anyone could have psychotic experiences in circumstances of extreme stress.

- The course and outcome of psychotic experiences are very different for different people. Less than a quarter of people who have distressing psychotic experiences at some time in their life remain permanently affected by them.

- People have poorer outcomes if their spouses or family members are highly critical or overprotective.

- Psychiatric diagnosis are labels that describe certain types of behaviour. They do not indicate anything about the nature or causes of experiences.

- Mental health and 'mental illness' (and different types of mental illness) shade into each other and are not separate categories.
- Ten to 15 percent of the population have heard voices or experienced hallucinations at some point in their life. These are frequently triggered by extreme experiences such as sleep deprivation.
- It may be appropriate to think in terms of stress-vulnerability when explaining psychotic experiences. People may have greater or lesser level of vulnerability to this type of experience, which are triggered by greater or fewer numbers of stressful events experienced.
- In some cultures hearing voices and seeing visions is seen as a spiritual gift rather than as a symptom of mental illness

Causes of psychotic experiences
- Social, biological and psychological causes of psychotic experiences are all important, and interact with one another.
- Because there is a very close relationship between 'mind' and 'brain', it is very difficult to draw clear lines between biological and psychological factors. The causes of

psychotic experiences are complex and one single cause' will not be found.

- Sometimes psychotic experiences can be triggered by something relatively minor but become a problem as a result of some kind of vicious circle involving the person's situation ort their reaction to the experience.

Biological factors in psychotic experiences

- In the main, research into genetics, brain chemistry, the physical environment and brain structure has not led to clear conclusions about physical causes.

- It is likely that genetics, brain chemistry, brain structure and the environment are all associated with vulnerabilities to a variety of general traits, which may be in turn be related to psychotic experiences.

Life circumstances and psychotic experiences

- Psychotic experiences can sometimes follow major events in someone's life, either negative (for example, bereavement) or positive (for example, winning the lottery).

- Many people who have psychotic experiences abuse or trauma at some point in their lives.
- If people who have who have mental health problems live in a calm and relaxed home atmosphere, there are less likely to return.

Psychological factors in psychotic experiences

- Psychological models of psychotic experiences focus on patterns of thought associated with these phenomena and on their meaning for the individual.
- These include: difficulties with attention, difficulties in understanding what other people are thinking, jumping to conclusions and the tendency to believe that the bad things that happen are the fault of other people, or of themselves.
- Hearing voices often appears to be the result of difficulty in distinguishing one's own, normal, inner speech from the words of other people.
- Psychotic experiences often have an important subjective meaning or significance for individual.

Cultural context of psychotic experiences

Societal, institutional and personal oppression as a cause of psychosis

- It has been suggested that the significant societal, institutionalised and personal oppressions which marginalised groups living in Britain often face (e.g. sexism, racism, classism, homophobia) and resulting social exclusion may in some people increase the likelihood of developing psychotic experiences.

- Such experiences may then bring them (voluntarily or involuntarily) into contact with mental health services, where similar oppressions exist at both an institutional and personal level.

- Exposure to these oppressions within a system which is meant to be helping people may then exacerbate the original distress and drive people into a spiral of increasing oppression and increasing psychosis and/or 'paranoia'.

- Workers who recognise the spiral of oppression and work in anti-discriminatory ways with users to acknowledge their issues and make sense of their distress may be able to fracture the spiral of oppression.

- The links between societal, institutional and personal oppressions require acknowledgement and further investigation.

- These socio-cultural aspects of vulnerability to psychosis are likely to have much in common with other experiences of abuse and marginalisation.

Cultural factors

- It is unclear whether people in all countries are equally likely to have psychotic experiences. However the World Health organization has reported that psychotic experiences occur in many different cultures and appear at least superficially to be similar even when the cultures are very different.

- People in different cultures describe psychological problems in different ways. For instance, in some cultures some psychological problems might be described in terms of physical pain or discomfort; in other cultures such experiences are described using emotional terms such as fears or anxiety.

- Cultural patterns may also influence the ways in which individuals explain their experiences. Unpleasant or upsetting experiences are often explained in terms of the beliefs that are common in that culture ('ghosts', 'the devil', 'space aliens' or 'evil eye').

- Sometimes explanations used by people from minority ethnic groups can be misinterpreted as psychosis if the context is not understood. In some cultures, for example, many people believe in the possibility of being possessed by demons. Sometimes someone's belief that he or she is possessed might be wrongly thought to be psychotic or delusional belief.

Racism

- People of African-Caribbean origin living in the UK are three times more likely to receive a diagnosis of schizophrenia than are white people.

- It has been suggested that the racism and social exclusion that Black people living in Britain often experience may increase the likelihood of them developing psychotic experiences.

- These socio-cultural aspects of vulnerability to psychosis are likely to have much in common with other experiences of abuse and marginalisation and require further investigation.

- Black people are almost likely to receive a diagnosis of schizophrenia than White people even if the experiences they describe are the same. The importance of taking the person's cultural context into account

- There is a huge diversity in what is considered an appropriate expression of distress in different cultures. If professionals are not sufficiently familiar with a person's culture, there is a risk that such expressions might be mistaken for psychotic experiences.

- This is also a danger with religious and spiritual beliefs and beliefs about spirit possession

- There is evidence that such misunderstandings are common. Part of the reason for this is that few mental health workers currently receive much training in cultural sensitivity, and there is an urgent need for such training.

- Mainstream services should also make links with local voluntary sector groups that have more expertise in this area. It is also well documented that the effects of racism are likely to increase vulnerability to developing psychotic experiences.

- There is also a tendency for prescription of higher doses of neuroleptic medication to Black people. Some researchers have linked this more ' heavy-handed 'approach to negative stereotypes of Black people as being more likely to be dangerous or violent.

- Mental health services have a poor record of engaging Black and minority ethnic people in long term care. Some research into Asian people's experience of services has revealed despair in relation to services, particularly by those unable to communicate in English. There is therefore a need for services to address the cultural needs of clients. This should include anti-discriminatory practice training for all mental health workers.

Chapter 61

QUALITY ASSURANCE FOR ANNUAL DEVELOPMENT

The home carried out Quality Assurance and Quality Control as an on- going policy or 1S0 9000. The condition of the building, its contents, the residents care and environment, all documents used such as policy, procedure, forms etc. need to be checked. Any areas identified that require improvement is dealt with, as part of the development plan and is prioritized. The manager carries out any improvements identified and major alteration (those that involve major finance) to discuss with the proprietor. The regular meeting (residents, staff, stakeholders, visitors, manager/proprietor helps with the Q-A).

Major development such as, building extension, alteration of building such as moving the wall or lift. Change of policy or environment that may affect the client such as change of category, must be discussed first with CSCI.

Chapter 62

RECORD KEEPING

All the staff must be able and willing to maintain records within the Home. It is important to keep records as evidence that an event has occurred. All records must be dated and signed by the writer and recorded in the appropriate book or form (see relevant policy and procedure).

All financial transactions must be witnessed and documented by two people.

All messages and telephone calls must be documented in the diary and passed on during the handover period and not on scraps of paper, which can become lost.

Client's files must be kept in a locked drawer. Information retained in them is confidential. Clients have the right to gain access to their own files if they so wish. (See Confidentiality Policy).

Chapter 63

RECORDING OF STAFF AND RESIDENTS MEETINGS

The following format is to be used:

Name of Home

Name of Meeting – e.g. Staff or Residents

Date

Time commenced

Time closed

Name of Chair

Persons Present

Apologies

The meeting was opened by (enter Chair's Name) at _____ (enter time). Everyone was thanked for their time and comments which will be discussed. The agenda was as follows:

Any comments raised by persons are to be documented as to whom raised them and what reply was given. The meeting records should not indicate ? all issues were raised by the Chair ? as if the meeting was a lecture.

Any issues that were raised during the last meeting and not dealt with should be raised again and the outcome documented.

The meeting should end:

All persons present were thanked for comments. The meeting was closed at _____ (time).

SUGGESTION TOPICS FOR RESIDENTS MEETINGS

1) Menus

Are clients happy with the menus? How food is served by staff. Any suggestions for menus?

2) Activities

Are clients happy with the present activity rota? Any suggestions for outings etc?

3) Welcome new clients to the Home since last meeting.

4) Keyworker   System

Do clients know who other keyworker is and their role?

5) Any changes which might be occurring in the Home in the near future e.g. building works

Chapter 64

POLICY STATEMENT OF THE RECRUITMENT
OF EX-OFFENDERS

- As an organisation using the Criminal Records Bureau (CRB) Disclosure service to assess applicants' suitability for positions of trust, The Home complies fully with the DBS Code of Practice and undertakes to treat all applicants for positions fairly. It undertakes not to discriminate unfairly against any subject of a Disclosure on the basis of conviction or other information revealed.

- The Home is committed to the fair treatment of its staff, potential staff or users of its services, regardless of race, gender, religion, sexual orientation, responsibilities for dependants, age, physical/mental disability or offending background.

- We actively promote equally of opportunity for all with the right mix of talent, skills and potential and welcome applications from a wide range of candidates, including those with criminal records. We select all candidates for interview based on their skills, qualifications and experience.

- A Disclosure is only requested after a thorough risk assessment has indicated that one is both proportionate and relevant to the position concerned. For those positions where a Disclosure is required, all application forms, job adverts and recruitment briefs will contain a statement that a Disclosure will be requested in the event of the individual being offered the position.

- Where a Disclosure is to form part of the recruitment process, we encourage all applicants called for interview to provide details of their criminal record at an early stage in the application process. We request that this information is sent under separate, confidential cover, to a designated person with The Home and we guarantee that this information is only seen by those who need to see it as part of the recruitment process.

- Unless the nature of the position allows The Home to ask questions about your entire criminal record we only ask about "unspent" convictions as defined in the Rehabilitation of Offenders Act 1974.

- We ensure that all those in The Home who are involved in the recruitment process have been suitably trained to identify and assess the relevance and circumstances of offences. We also ensure that they have received appropriate guidance and training in the relevant legislation relating to the employment of ex-offenders, e.g. the Rehabilitation of Offenders Act 1974.

- At interview, or in a separate discussion, we ensure that an open and measured discussion takes place on the subject of any offences or other matter that might be relevant to the position. Failure to reveal information that is directly relevant to the position sought could lead to withdrawal of an offer of employment.

- We make every subject of a DBS Disclosure aware of the existence of the DBS Code of Practice and make a copy available on request.

- We undertake to discuss any matter revealed in a Disclosure with the person seeking the position before withdrawing a conditional offer of employment.

- The Residents at The Home have a right to be cared for by suitable staff and the Home will endeavour to provide this.

- Having a criminal record will not necessarily bar you from working with us. This will depend on the nature of the position and the circumstances and background of your offences. Each applicant who has offences will be individually assessed by the Manager, so that our clients are not put at risk.

Chapter 65

RECRUITMENT OF STAFF

When the home advertises for staff the following legislation will be adhered to :

- Equal Opportunities
- The Race Relations Act 1976
- Health & Safety Act 1974
- The Rehabilitation of Offenders Act 1974
- Sex Discrimination Act 1976
- Disability Discrimination Act 1996
- Employment Right Act 1996
- The National Care Standards 2000

When vacancies of any grade arise, the following steps are taken:

1) Internal advertisement on the staff notice board for seven days – usually management positions.

   Internal applicants are interviewed within 7 days.

   If there is no successful applicant internally.

2) The management will advertise in the local newspapers for up to 2 weeks or in national care papers for 2 weeks if the response from the local newspaper is not satisfactory.

All applicants must:

1) Complete application form attach copies of CV and any qualifications. Original certificates will need to be brought to the interview. The previous 5-year work history must be completed. The manager must investigate any gaps.

2) The Applicant is interviewed by the manager. The job description of the vacant post is given to the applicant and the person specification.

3) A minimum of 2 references are taken:

a) employer

b) Character

In some cases:

c) Doctors

In all cases:

d) Clearance from Criminal Investigations Bureau including a POVA check.

e) Staff will be expected to have completed or intend to complete their NVQ at the level to which post they are applying.

f) A passport size photograph

g)   Proof of ID e.g. passport, driving license

h)   Proof of address (usually by a utility bill or bank statement).

i)   If candidate is not a UK resident, they must produce evidence that they are eligible to work in the UK

4) Interview

Completion of the application form is brought to the interview. The manager checks that all questions are answered fully and that the completed form has the name, address and telephone number of 2 referees. This form will enable the manager to assess the applicant's ability to communicate clearly.

The manager will go through the form and discuss previous 5-year employment and any gaps in employment history. Relevant scenarios will be given in order to assess the applicant's suitability for the post applied for. Open and closed questioning will be used during the interview.

The interviewer will explain the general routines of the homes shift times and the client's which the home is registered for. Key working and the homes aims, and objectives are also discussed. The applicant is given the opportunity throughout the interview to ask questions and discuss the post at length.

Interview notes will be kept and if the applicant is employed these will be kept in his/her staff file.

Applicants must declare if they are related to the management of any staff member or resident. Applications will be followed up by a request for a written references. All prospective staff must complete a DBS form, once the forms are received a POVA request may be made. The candidate can be considered for employment the usual trial period will commence upon a satisfactory written reference being received.

Staff employed must sign the contract on their first day.

Staff are given an induction pack containing the key procedures e.g., accident, missing persons, fire and health and safety.

Induction programmed is implemented. Each new employee will be assigned to a mentor – being a senior staff they will work frequently with. The mentor will be responsible for assisting the new employee in settling in and ensuring that key policies and routines are explained. The skills for skill induction standards must be completed within 12 weeks of employment.

Redundancy

The company reserves the right to make any staff redundant when reasonable notice will be given and entitlement according to the current legislation will be paid.

Chapter 66

RESTRAINT

It is not the Home's policy to encourage use of restraint, but it is also recognised that there may be incidents where it is a last resort and necessary to use in specific incidents.

Minimal restraint must only be used if:

a)   A person is self-harming

b)   A resident is physically attacking another person to the extent that if you do not intervene serious harm to another individual could occur.

Prohibited Restraint Practices

1)   No person must hold another around the neck or head area – or block their airways.

2)   No limbs of fingers etc are to extend – such this could cause breakage of these bones.

3)   A person must *never* be physically struck

If the situation is unable to be controlled or there is not enough resources in the home then the Police must be called to intervene. All other residents must be advised to leave the area and the staff should be allocated by the Person in charge to offer reassurance to the people.

If possible the person who is being physically aggressive must be encouraged to stay in an area away from other clients and allowed to calm down. The GP must be notified, and his advice sought. The person on call and the next of kin are to be notified.

A full report of the incident must be recorded in the

a)   Incident Book

b)   Care   notes   stating   exact circumstances

Any such incidents are regarded are reportable and therefore The National Care Standards Commission must be notified within 24 hours of the event

If necessary the duty approved social worker and duty psychiatrist may be notified. It may be the person could be required to be detained under Mental Health Act 1983.

If the psychiatrist regularly sees the person then he is to be notified within 24 hours.

Also see policy on handling aggressive residents.

Chapter 67

RISK

definition

RISK is to take chance. Risk is danger, hazard, jeopardy, gamble, pitfall. It is an individual right to take a risk. Without risk life is tedious.

A person undertakes a task which could result in injury e.g.

Going for a walk

Having a bath

Administering their own drugs.

Use of the kitchen and appliances.

Travelling by public or private transport.

Managing their own affairs e.g. finance

Keeping their own valuables in the home.

Drinking alcohol and smoking.

Verbal and physical aggression towards other residents resulting in retaliation.

in order to withdraw or restrict residents taking risks the management should;

1. Assess the needs of individual residents i.e. what they can and cannot do themselves and they need help.

2. Obtain the residents permission and if possible in their presence discuss with their

next of kin, the doctor, or outside agencies as to the danger to the resident and others and whether the risk and potential danger outweigh the residents needs

3. The resident should be informed as to the implication to the community, also of the implication of the risk associated with the choice to the resident.

The staff should evaluate and monitor each resident's condition and behaviour so as to ensure that a reasonable balance is achieved between independence and risk taking and create safeguards to ensure that any limitations placed on residents scope to act independently are minimum, explained, justified, and reviewed regularly. Manager should inform, instruct and train staff about the risk and the precautions to be taken.

Chapter 68

MAINTAINING SAFE WORKING PRACTICE

The home has published literature on the following Legislation:

- Health and Safety at Work Act 1974
- Management of Health and Safety at Work Regulations 1999
- Work place (Health, Safety, and Welfare) Regulations 1992
- Provision and use of Work Equipment Regulations 1992
- Electricity at Work Regulations 1989
- Health and Safety (First Aid) Regulations 1981
- Control of Substances Hazardous to Health Regulations (COSHH) 1988
- Manual Handling Operations Regulations 1992

  Reporting of injuries, Diseases and Dangerous Occurrences Regulations (RIDDOR) 1985

All staff must read and adhere to this legislation as to ensure the Home provides a safe environment for the residents, staff and visitors to the Home. It is the responsibility of the proprietor to ensure that policies and procedures are in place. It is staff responsibility to adhere to these and to report to the manager any unsafe working practices or hazards identified throughout the building and its grounds.

Staff must not participate in any activity which may cause harm to themselves or to clients. Risk Assessments must be read and how these risks can be reduced must be implemented.

Staff must not allow persons to enter the Home without checking their ID or confirming who they are.

Chapter 69

SECURITY

OBJECTIVE

To ensure that all care assistants are fully conversant with an agreed policy on security which should not conflict with the objective of the mobility policy.

QUESTIONS

1. Is there a clearly defined policy on the routine to be followed in the event of an accident or fall?

2. Are all staff acquainted with this policy?

3. Is there any procedure for restraint of residents, should this be necessary and been agreed jointly by medical and caring staff and adopted as a management policy?

4. Are all efforts being made to ensure that measures adopted in the interest of security are not undermining residents' dignity, mobility or other important factors?

4. Are all efforts being made to ensure that measures adopted in the interest of security are not undermining residents' dignity, mobility or other important factors?

SOME POINTS TO CONSIDER

1. In the event of an accident or fall staff should give appropriate help to the resident, inform the on-call staff, manager or proprietor.

2. Inform the doctor and others concerned and note details on the standard form.

3. Staff should not be blamed for accidents that occur when they are acting according to policy, taking care and reasonable precautions.

4. Restraints by chair trays and safety sides should not ever be used other than in exceptional cases when the decision should be jointly made by the team or jointly by medical and care staff. No resident should be restrained by means of a harness or anything. I must express my main concern that no resident should be restrained in any of my homes without the consent of medical practitioners or management team if possible discuss with the resident, next of kin or registration officers. In my opinion, if the resident needs to be retrained it may need to be only for a very short period, say up to 2 days,

after which time consideration must be taken in transferring the resident to another home.

Some other points that staff need to consider on security are:

- Safety factors in the residents' care
- Legal implications
- Home policy
- Fire precautions
- Complaint procedure
- Proper use of equipment

If possible one could get advice from the director, the health and safety officer or the local authority's domestic supervisor.

Chapter 70

STAFF APPRAISAL

It is really self-explanatory – a process by which there is a record to show that on a regular basis each employee is assessed (appraised) as to their levels of competence in relation to the duties allocated to them and within set targets for achievement. This is a formal process and it should be conducted annually, ideally based upon the person's employment start date. It should always be done in the presence of the person being appraised. The 'Appraisal' should be structured and follow a consistent format. At the start, targets set at the time of the previous appraisal should be identified and an assessment made of the level of success or otherwise in meeting such targets – noting any reasons for failure to achieve. Then the specific and general responsibilities allocated to the staff member should be listed and gone through one by one with comments being made in respect of competency levels attained including areas where both higher and lower than expected levels have been achieved. Then, targets for the coming year should be agreed and set, including any to be carried forward from the previous year. Specific training objectives should be identified either as a part of the general development of the employee, or to address any particular deficiencies identified as a part of the appraisal process. Finally, the employee should be given the opportunity to make any observations of their own about any aspect of their employment and that are in addition to the areas already discussed. Staff must identify their own strengths and weaknesses, aims/objectives for the forthcoming year.

Record of Appraisal:

As with supervision, it is recommended that a standard pre-printed format is devised for use in carrying out appraisals. As before, this should contain basic information including the names of the manager, the employee and the date the appraisal is carried out. Separate areas should be included in the form that will encompass all the matters described in the paragraph above. On completion the form should be signed by both parties and a copy given to the employee with the main form being retained on their personal staff file

Chapter 71

STAFF COMPLAINTS PROCEDURE

In the event of any complaints it will be looked into by a representative of the management and a decision will be made.

The member of staff who may have complained should be prepared to put it either verbally or in writing to the management. Having done so the management will deal with it and the finding will be given either verbally or in writing.

Below are steps we advise to take in case of any complaints, the procedure should be as follows:

STEP 1 If you have a complaint, it should be made verbally or in writing in the first instance to the manager or if the complaint is about the manager, the complainant should report it or the general manager or proprietor.

STEP 2 If the Manager fails to settle your complaint within 7 days' time, then your complaint should be put to the Proprietor in writing, whose name and address are shown on the Registration Certificate displayed prominently in the Home.

STEP 3 If your complaint is still not dealt with to your satisfaction, then a complaint about management of the Home can be made in writing to:

Commission for Social Care Inspection

STEP 4   If you become dissatisfied with the way your complaint about the management of the Home has been dealt with by the Inspection Officer

STEP 5 At any stage of a complaint, the complainant may contact CSCI.

Staff must know the current inspection officer from CSCI responsible for the Residential Home.

Under no circumstances should staff be contacted at their home regarding a complaint unless requested to do so by the management.

Any complaint can be made directly to CSCI at any stage.

Chapter 72

STAFF SUPERVISION

As per NCS,(National are standard) staff supervision will be held at least six times per year. The manager will oversee staff's actual work and will liaise with the new staff mentor as the how the new member is progressing. Formal supervision will begin after the first 4 weeks and be held on a one to one basis. This session will be recorded by the supervisor and signed by the supervisor and supervisee copies will be retained by both parties. The session will involve, testing staff's knowledge and understanding of policies, procedures, specific client needs and any other relevant duties within the workplace. Supervisors must record which policy client etc they have discussed. The supervisee can also express their own difficulties and strengths – which in doing, should be identify the staff's own training needs. These can then be assessed at to how they can be met either internally or externally, depending on the staff's training needs, their position within the Home and experience; this will also determine the frequency of formal supervision. The supervisor is to check that all correct documentation is completed as per the list on the staff forms. Check Topps book and knowledge of Policies and Procedures form that progress in being made. The supervisor should discuss staff punctuality, sickness record as to whether there has been a concern.

The supervision session gives both parties the opportunity to express their opinion and views. If the supervisor is unable to answer queries then this must be passed into their line manager to deal with

For most staff supervisor sessions will be held at 2 monthly intervals unless more frequent if there are concerns or issues which need addressing.

Chapter 73

TERMS OF CONDITIONS OF EMPLOYMENT

The management hereby offers full/part-time employment to:

This will become void if it comes to the notice of management that the applicant has given false information or failed to give any information in writing which in his/her opinion would have prevented the applicant being offered the post.

Mrs _____

In the capacity of _____

This employment commences on _____(am/pm)

If full-time state hours ____if part-time state minimum hours _____

REMUNERATION

At the rate of £ _____ per hour to be paid monthly by cheque/cash.

Excluding/Including Income Tax and National Insurance contributions.

A wages review will take place annually.

CRIMINAL RECORDS BUREAU/DBS

All posts are subject to a check made by the Criminal Records Bureau which is to be paid by the employee.

ANNUAL LEAVE

As per present Government guidelines.

How much annual leave are workers entitled to? Most workers, whether part-time or full-time, are legally entitled to 4.8 weeks' paid annual leave. Additional annual leave may be agreed as part of a worker's contract. A week's leave should allow workers to be away from work for a week - i.e. it should be the same amount of time as the working week. If a worker does a five-day week, they are entitled to 24 days leave. If a worker does a three-day week, the entitlement is 14.4 days leave. Employers can set the times that workers take their leave, for example for a Christmas shutdown. If a worker's employment ends, they have the right to be paid for the leave time due and not taken. Unpaid leave can be taken within the year by arrangement with the Proprietor/Manager.

MATERNITY LEAVE

Statutory Maternity Pay is a weekly payment that you may be able to get from your employer. You must meet qualifying conditions based on the length of your employment with your employer and how much you earn. The amount of SMP you get also depends on how much you earn.

How to get SMP (Statutory maternity Pay)

If you are pregnant and you think you are eligible for SMP from your employer, you must tell your employer that you intend to stop work to have the baby and the day you want your SMP to start. You must also provide your employer with evidence of when your baby is due.

Telling your employer

Most women will be able to take maternity leave from their work (see advice on the DBERR website). To claim maternity leave you must tell your employer no later than the end of the qualifying week that you:

- are pregnant
- the date you expect your baby
- the date you want to start your maternity leave.

If you can get both maternity leave and SMP it is best to tell your employer, the date you want your SMP to start at the same time as you tell your employer about your leave.

You must, though, give your employer at least 28 days' notice of the date you want your SMP to start. Your employer may need your notice in writing. If it is not possible to give 28 days' notice, you must tell your employer as soon as you can. If your employer considers it was reasonably practicable for you to have given notice earlier than you did, they can refuse to pay you SMP.

If your baby is born prematurely, before you had given notice to your employer, you may still be able to get SMP.

Paternity Leave

Paternity leave and pay is available to employees following the placement of a child for adoption..

Following the birth of a child, the new rights to paternity leave and pay will give eligible employees the right to take paid leave to care for the child or support the mother.

Eligibility

Employees must satisfy the following conditions in order to qualify for paternity leave. They must:

- have or expect to have responsibility for the child's upbringing
- be the biological father of the child or the mother's husband or partner
- have worked continuously for their employer for 26 weeks ending with the 15th week before the baby is due

Employers can ask their employees to provide a self-certificate (see below for further details) as evidence that they meet these eligibility conditions. Length of paternity, leave. Eligible employees can choose to take either one week or two consecutive weeks' paternity leave (not odd days).

They can choose to start their leave:

- from the date of the child's birth (whether this is earlier or later than expected), or
- from a chosen number of days or weeks after the date of the child's birth (whether this is earlier or later than expected), or
- from a chosen date later than the first day of the week in which the baby is expected to be born.

Leave can start on any day of the week on or following the child's birth but must be completed:

within 56 days of the actual date of birth of the child, or if the child is born early, within the period from the actual date of birth up to 56 days after the first day of the expected week of birth.

Only one period of leave is available to employees irrespective of whether more than one child is born as the result of the same pregnancy. Statutory Paternity

During their paternity leave, most employees are entitled to Statutory Paternity Pay (SPP) from their employers.

Statutory Paternity Pay is paid by employers for either one or two consecutive weeks as the employee has chosen. The rate of

Statutory Paternity Pay is the same as the standard

rate of Statutory Maternity Pay – from

April 2005, this is £106 a week or 90% of pay Employees who have average weekly earnings below the Lower Earnings Limit for National Insurance purposes (£82 a week from April 2005) do not qualify for SPP. Employees who do not qualify for SPP, or who are normally low-paid, may be able to get Income Support while on paternity leave. Additional financial support may be available through Housing Benefit, Council Tax Benefit, Tax Credits or a Sure Start Maternity Grant. Further information is available from your local Jobcentre Plus office or Social Security office.

Notice of intention to take paternity leave

Employees must inform their employers of their intention to take paternity leave by the end of the fifteenth week before the baby is expected, unless this is not reasonably practicable. They must tell their employers:

> the week the baby is due whether they wish to take one- or two-weeks' leave when they want their leave to start.

Employees can change their mind about the date on which they want their leave to start providing they tell their employer at least 28 days in advance (unless this is not reasonably practicable). Employees must tell their employers the date they expect any payments of SPP to start at least 28 days in advance, unless this is not reasonably practicable.

SICK PAY

If Tax/National Insurance is deducted then SSP entitlement is automatically paid on the production of Self Certification or a Medical Certificate. If employment period is less than 6 months the claimant should apply to the DSS for SSP. Employee may be requested to apply to DSS for SSP even if employment is more than 6 months.

Persistent intermittent sickness on self-certificate will require verification from the GP of good health at the person's own expense and medical clearance must be obtained before reinstatement of employment. If a period of sickness exceeds one week a medical certificate will be required.

Some types of sickness leave which are lengthy (operations, etc.) will require a review of the person's job description as well as a certificate of good health and capacity to do the job will be required before reinstatement of employment. Other options of employment within the Home may be applicable.

REFERENCES

Staff may be employed, and their contractual rights respected pending two written references, received before employment. One reference being from a previous employer and one-character reference. According to the national minimum standards for Care Homes Standard 29.1. However if the manager after receiving satisfactory verbal reference may employ you subject to the two references received within one month. If not the management reserves the right to withdraw employment.

All staff employed will have a trial period of 4 to six weeks for both their benefit and the Home's. After which, when references are received or if already received, full contractual employment will be offered, or termination decided by one or both parties. The trial period may be shortened or extended at the discretion of the management. During or after this period the management reserves the right to terminate employment giving 24 hours' notice

DOCUMENTS

The employee must show originals of the following documents before offer of employment, copies will be retained by the Home.

6) Passport (and work permit if applicable or proof to work in the UK)

7) Evidence of address

8) A completed Health Questionnaire

9) Birth Certificate (if an original birth certificate is not available, evidence that a copy has been applied for)

10) A passport size photograph

Failure to produce these documents will result in the employee not being offered a contract.

TRAINING

All staff should ensure they are aware of the following with 7 days of employment:

a) The Health and Safety at Work Act.

b) Fire Precaution, Prevention and Emergency Procedure in the event of fire.

c) The record of instruction and Skills for Care induction as prepared by the management.

Employees must be willing to attend courses which the CSCI and management indicate is necessary to care for our Service User.

TERMINATION

Employment may be terminated by one month's notice on either side.

The Proprietor reserves the right to terminate employment without giving full notice for misconduct or behaviour not compatible with the aims of the establishment.

The Home operates an instant dismissal policy for serious misconduct, breach of confidentiality or behaviour not compatible with the aims of the establishment, which does not require a verbal or written warning.

ROUTINE

The Proprietor and Manager's instructions are to be carried out without hindrance at all times in respect of routine, policy, including any changes therein, aims and objectives of the Home as per job description. (In the absence of the Manager, the Proprietor, the General Manager or the Deputy Manager may act for the Manager.)

The Manager must be prepared to provide reasonable physical, environmental and psychological care to the Service Users.

VALUABLES

The Home accepts no responsibility for money, valuables and possessions brought into the Home by staff, being stolen or damaged, whilst staff is on duty. Such as items brought into the Home are entirely at the person's own risk.

STAFF / TEAM MEETINGS

Staff must be prepared to attend meetings held by the Home. Failure to attend such meetings will result in the management taking disciplinary action.

CODE OF CONDUCT

Staff must act always in a professional manner whilst on duty or when representing the home. They must use appropriate language and not swear. Service Users must not ever be called by Nick names. The Home will not tolerate any form of service user abuse.

Alcohol or illegal substances must not be used whilst on duty.

Smoking

The Health Bill devolves regulation-making powers on this issue to the Welsh Assembly. The Smoke Free Premises etc. (Wales) Regulations 2007 came into force on the 2nd of April, and there are very few exemptions to the smoking ban and anyone who breaches the law could face heavy penalties. Employers, managers and those in control of premises will need to display no-smoking notices and take reasonable steps to ensure that staff, customers, members and visitors are aware of the new law and do not smoke in buildings.

Premises exempt from smoke free legislation
Health and Safety legislation will continue to require employers, in premises permitted exemptions under the smoke-free law, to reduce the risk to the health and safety of their employees from second hand smoking to as low a level as is reasonably practicable.

All Service Users, Service Users, service users, other staff and visitors to the home must be treated in a respectful, courteous and in an anti-discriminatory manner.

Policy - Abide by the policy of the Home and the instructions therein at all times.

Effective communication must be used.

Messages must be recorded in the diary and not on a piece of paper. These must be passed on to the relevant person or during handover. All notes concerning Service Users are to be recorded in relevant places.

Confidentiality - Information pertaining to the Service Users/ Staff and Proprietor should not be disclosed to any enquirer or be given to anybody within or outside the Home without the Manager's /Proprietor's consent or written signed permission - refer to Policy of the Home.

Appearance & Presentation - Staff should present themselves for duty clean and tidy. Female staff must not wear jeans during day duty. No shorts or miniskirts. Female night staff may wear trousers.

Long hair should be tied back. Suitable, comfortable footwear must be worn (no high heels, boots or opened toed shoes without backings). Rings with sharp surfaces, nail varnish, long nails are not allowed; any damage inflicted upon Service Users will be viewed as a serious matter.

Punctuality - Must be on time for work. Must be prepared to stay until other staff have taken over before going of duty.

Chapter 74

DISCIPLINARY CODE

A   PURPOSE AND SCOPE

Whilst it is sometimes necessary to discipline and in extreme cases dismiss an employee. The main purpose of the disciplinary procedure is to help and encourage all employees to achieve and maintain standards of conduct attendance and job performance. The aim is to ensure consistent and fair treatment for all.

B   GENERAL PRINCIPLES

1   This Code shall cover all employees with the exception of new employees working on a probationary period.

2   All employees when permanently engaged will be given a copy of their Terms and Conditions of Employment and of this procedure and it is their duty to ensure that these are fully understood.

3   No disciplinary action will be taken against an employee until the case has been fully investigated.

4   At every stage in the procedure the employee will be advised of the nature of the complaint against him or her. The employee will be given the opportunity to

state his or her case before any decision is made.

5   At all stages the employee will have the right to be accompanied by a shop steward employee representative or work colleague during the disciplinary interview.

6   No employee will be dismissed for a first breach of discipline except in the case of gross misconduct when the penalty will be dismissal without notice or payment in lieu of notice.

7   An employee will have the right to appeal against any disciplinary penalty imposed.

8   The procedure may be implemented at any stage if the employee's alleged misconduct warrants such action.

9   Since dismissal is the ultimate sanction it is anticipated that its use will be confined to rare cases. There will be no dismissal without the specific authority of the Proprietor.

C PROCEDURE

Before the implementation of the formal procedure informal discussions and counselling will take place to establish whether the problem is in fact a disciplinary one and may be dealt with by other means.

Where initial discussions establish that the matter is more serious or may involve repeated minor errors the following procedure will be used. At every stage hereafter the Manager will be consulted before any decision is taken to ensure that the procedure has been complied with.

Any warning whether written or oral will remain valid for a period of 12 months. In the event that the employee's performance is satisfactory throughout that period the warning and any previous warnings shall upon expiry of the period be disregarded for disciplinary purposes.

Stage 1   Oral Warning

If conduct or performance does not meet acceptable standards the Manager will interview the employee and if appropriate give the employee a formal oral warning. He or she will be advised of the reason for the warning that it is the first stage of the disciplinary procedure and of his or her right of appeal. A brief note of the oral warning will be kept.

Stage 2   First Written Warning

In the event of the conduct complained of not being rectified or in the event of a further offence there will be a further discussion between the Manager and the Employee. The Manager will give a written warning specifying the conduct complained of and a time limit for improvement. It will warn that action under stage 3 will be considered if there is no satisfactory improvement and will advise of the right of appeal. The warning will be confirmed in writing and a copy sent to the Proprietor.

Stage 3   Final Warning

In the event of the conduct complained of still not being rectified or in the event of further misconduct there will be a further meeting between the Manager and the employee at which a further written warning will be given to the employee specifying:-

    (a)   A clear statement of that conduct

    (b)   A plan and time limit for improvement

(c)   That disciplinary action involving redeployment demotion or

Dismissal (as the case may be) could result if there is not

Improvement within the specified time limit or if there is a

Recurrence of the misconduct.

When the action has been taken a copy of the warning given to the employee together with any relevant information is placed in the employee's record.   The employee should acknowledge receipt of this warning in writing.

Stage 4   Redeployment   Demotions   or Dismissal

Disciplinary Interview

In the event of the conduct complained of not being rectified or in the event of gross misconduct the Manager shall carry out a full investigation into the relevant facts and a disciplinary interview shall be held at which the employee the Manager and the General Manager shall be present.

An employee may be suspended on full pay pending the investigation and the disciplinary interview.

The employee shall be given 2 clear days' notice in writing of the disciplinary interview and such notice shall state that disciplinary action including dismissal may be taken against the employee as a result of the interview.

The interview shall be conducted by the Manager who shall inform the employee of the details of the conduct being complained of and the results of his investigation. The employee shall then be given an opportunity of explanation.

The Manager and the General Manager shall then decide whether further investigation is required and if it is shall adjourn the interview and reconvene when the investigation is completed.

Following the interview the Manager and General Manager shall decide what disciplinary action if any is appropriate and shall notify the employee in writing of their decision the reasons and the employee's right of appeal. If dismissal is deemed appropriate the General Manager shall obtain the specific authority of the Proprietor.

Types of Disciplinary Action

      (a)   Suspension

               Suspension from work can be without pay and for a period of between 2 and 5 days depending on the circumstances. If an employee is absent due to sickness on the days when suspension falls due the suspension will be served after his/her return.

(b)   Redeployment Demotion and Down Grading

In certain circumstances where misconduct amounts to a breach of responsibility or failure to reach normally accepted standards the Company may demote transfer redeploy or otherwise down-grade an employee as an alternative to suspension or dismissal.

(c)   Dismissal

If conduct or performance is still unsatisfactory and the employee still fails to reach the prescribed standards dismissal will normally result. There will be no dismissal without the specific authority of the Proprietor.

Gross Misconduct

Some offences may be judged as gross misconduct in which case dismissal without previous warnings will normally result. The following are examples of gross misconduct:-

(a)   Theft fraud deliberate falsification of records

(b)   Assault on another person

(c)   Deliberate damage to company property

(d)   Serious incapability through alcohol or being under the influence

of illegal drugs

(e)   Serious negligence which causes unacceptable loss damage or

Injury

(f)   Breaking of confidentiality policy

(g)   Serious act of insubordination

(h)   Neglect of Service User

(i)   Serious abuse of Service Users

When an allegation of gross misconduct is raised the employee shall be suspended on full pay and told when to attend a disciplinary interview. The matter will then be dealt with as specified in Stage 4 above.

If on completion of the investigation and the full disciplinary procedure the Company is satisfied that the employee is guilty of gross misconduct the result will normally be summary dismissal without notice or payment in lieu of notice.

D   APPEALS AGAINST THE DISCIPLINARY ACTION

1   If an employee wishes to appeal against disciplinary action other than dismissal he/she has the right of appeal to the Proprietor.

2   Appeal should always be made by notice in writing sent to the Proprietor and is to be made within 5 working days of receipt of notification of the disciplinary action or the issue of warning.

3   Further appeal may be made to the Proprietor upon notice in writing given to the Proprietor and is to be made within 5 working days of the decision being appealed against.   Appeal against the Proprietor must be made to CSCI directly.

4   Appeal against dismissal should be made to the Proprietor in writing within 5 working days of dismissal. If the appeal is upheld the employee will be reinstated to his or her former post.

5   The decision of the Proprietor is final

E   GRIEVANCE PROCEDURE

1   Initial Action

The employee should raise the matter orally or in writing with the Manager. The Manager will either take a decision on the matter or if he thinks it appropriate refer it to the General Manager. The decision will be given to the employee within 2 days the Manager shall make a short report for the information of the Proprietor.

2   Appeal

If the employee wishes to appeal against a decision of the Manager he/she has the right of appeal to the General Manager and then a further right of appeal to the Proprietor.

3   Employee Representative

An employee may be accompanied at any of the interviews or appeals if he/she so wishes by a shop steward employee representative or work colleague.

4   Mode of Appeal

(a)   Appeal should always be made by notice in writing to the General

Manager or Proprietor as appropriate within 5 working

days of a decision being appealed against.

(b)   The decision of the Proprietor is final.

COMPLAINTS

The person must put his or her grievance or complaint in writing (in English) to the Proprietor within 3 days of the event. The Proprietor and her representative will acknowledge with 3 days and reply within 14 days of receipt. If there is any delay you will be given a reason verbally or in writing e.g. delay in investigation. If the person is still not happy with the initial response he/she must put this is writing to the proprietor within 3 days of receipt.

The proprietor or his representative will endeavour to carry out an investigation and reply within 28 days of given the person a reason.

If the person is not happy with the internal investigation (proprietor's reply) he/she must inform the proprietor in writing and if they decide to continue the complaint proceeding this must be done within 14 days. After that the home will consider the matter closed.

Having said the above, the individual has the right to make their complaint to the Inspection Unit or see changes to Complaints and Procedure document. The current name and address and telephone of the Commission for Social Care Inspection is: csci

If still not happy with the Inspectors decision you may approach the Citizens Advice Bureau, current address

Citizens Advice Bureau

or   Local Ombudsman

Lastly we wish to make it clear that any person that makes a complaint will not be discriminated or prejudiced against.

PERSONAL DETAILS

National Insurance Number

P45 Produced   (Date)

Not Produced   (Date)

Date of Birth

Address

Telephone

Next of Kin

Address

Telephone

Work   Telephone

I, the undersigned confirm that I have read the job description attached and will implement it and the contents of this contract. I undertake to read and implement the Homes Policies within one month of my employment as listed within the Induction Pack and all other Home Policies within three months.

Signature

Manager's Signature

Proprietor's Signature

Date:

Chapter 75

THE WRITING OF CARE NOTES

1. All clients must have an entry made in their daily care notes at least once a day. Care notes must be written corresponding to the care plan as to ensure staff are meeting their individual needs. First write the date and then the number of the care plan the entry is relating to. When you finish writing you must sign your initial and surname. Do not leave spaces or empty lines between your entry and your signature. Ensure your entry has given enough information for others to be able to look back on and be clear about what has happened. Remember these are legal documents.

2. If a resident complains of feeling unwell - what have you done about it? Example:

   - Mrs A complains of a headache
   - Was pain relief offered/ refused? (Check medication records first for PRN medication

and whether they have already had pain relief).

- Was blood pressure taken?
- If urine is strong or offensive were fluids encouraged?
- Was GP informed?
- If legs are swollen, was resident advised to elevate legs?
- If a client is a diabetic, what is their blood sugar?
- If a resident complains of diarrhoea
- Is it overflow? When was this?
- Was a laxative offered? By not writing what you have done about a complaint of ill health is considered as neglect.

3. If a resident who is not usually incontinent of urine is on occasion, then have staff checked colour, consistency of urine. If problem persists has the doctor be contacted to eliminate a urine infection or other urinary problems.

4. Any PRN medication that is given, the drug name, reason given, and the time given is to be stated. If a PRN tranquilliser is given then who authorised it should also be stated.

5. Any household remedy administered should be written in notes – check residents who request painkillers, that they are already not on other

painkillers which are of the same group., e.g., persons on co-proxamol, co-dydrmol, co-codraymol cannot have paracetamol as these drugs already contain paracetamol

6. Residents should never be told to do anything- they are to be advised or encouraged, etc. It is acceptable is a resident's behaviour is disturbing to others for them to be asked to leave that particular area. They are not to be told to go to their rooms – as if it is punishment.

7. If a resident is abusive or is swearing the actual content of the conversation is not necessary i.e. words like "bitch" do not need to be written in the notes.

8. If a resident is seen by an official visitor e.g. doctor, CPN, Care Manager, District Nurse their name and the reason for the visit should be put in the notes. It is not acceptable to write "seen by doctor – prescribed .... This doesn't tell anyone the name of the doctor or why the doctor visited or what the prescription is   for.
All residents who see a doctor at hospital the

name of the Doctor, what department and hospital they were seen.

9. When a client goes out, the time they went and returned is to noted and where they are going if you know.

10. How the residents spend their day is to be recorded and if they have taken part in any activities the person who held the activity session should be recorded as well as the actual activity. " Do not write participated in Homes activity" this is not giving enough information.

11. All accidents or incidents must be recorded giving full information

12. If a resident is found smoking in his/her room – it is acceptable to ASK the resident to give their cigarettes in to the office. Staff cannot take away other's cigarettes – again this would be punishment, this needs to be agreed in the Care Plan. (If management feel unhappy with resident smoking, they could only warn residents using the contract, which they signed and if necessary give notice to leave).

13. Staff must ensure they take and record appropriate action, as to ensure evidence of your actions.

Chapter 76

TOILETING

1. Some Reasons Why Clients May Need Toileting

Tendency to be incontinent due to:

a) Prostrate enlargement frequency, urgency, dribbling

b) Neurological damage, e.g., stroke

c) Urinary tract infection or cystitis

d) Dementia

e) Psychological e.g. depressed, unmotivated, attention seeking

f) Other urinary problems

g) Laziness

2. Aim

To reduce incontinency and promote independence.

3. Assessment

a) Frequency of incontinency

b) Whether it is urinary or faecal incontinence

c) Can resident go to the toilet themselves or do they need an escort or just prompting

d) Should advice be sought from the G.P. and continence advisor

4. Care Plan

Individual needs to be added to care plan

5. Procedure

a) *Preparation of the Resident*

Discuss and agree with the resident the procedure which should be followed. Encourage the resident to persevere with the routine e.g. to toilet himself/herself.

If the resident is in the lounge then you should avoid asking them "to come to the toilet - or let's go to the toilet so I can change your pad - *think* how would you feel? It is a personal problem being advertised to everyone. Staff should not bring the pads into the lounge with them. A discreet word in the client's ear that you would like to speak to them outside is sufficient.

b) *Preparation of Environment and Items Required*

If the client is known to wear an Incooped then this should be in the toilet already - with a flannel, towel, soap, gloves and disposable white bag. The resident can be escorted to the toilet. If assurance is needed - the door should be locked, the windows closed, and the curtains pulled. The client may not wish staff to be there whilst using the toilet - this wish should be respected.

c)   *Procedure*

- Escort to the toilet
- Assistance with underwear if needed
- Wash genital area
- Soiled pad should be discarded in a white bag which should be put in a yellow bag and put in clinical waste bin outside.

6.   After Client Has Been Toileted

a)   Staff and client must wash and dry their hands

b)   Escort   client   back   to
bedroom/lounge.

c)   Tidy the environment for the next
client.

d)   Ensure used flannel and towel are
taken to the laundry for washing.

Chapter 77

SKILLS FOR CARE – INDUCTION STANDARDS

The foundation standards are requirements of the Care Standards Act 2000 and is specifically linked to standards relating to training within the National Minimum Standards which state and require that: All staff receive induction training to NTO (National Training Organisation) specification within the first 12 weeks of appointment, which equips them to meet assessed needs of the service users accommodated, as defined in their individual plan of care.

There are five foundation standards, these are:

- Understand how to apply the value base of care
- Communicate effectively
- Develop as a worker
- Recognise and respond to abuse and neglect

- Understand the experiences and particular needs of the individuals using the service

  Every standard reflects a different part of a person's job. They are not a list of training they are about the employee/carer showing they have achieved a level of understanding that is required to do their job.

All new employees will be allocated a mentor to assist them to complete our skills for care training programme. Any training needs will be identified during staff supervision and documented to show how these can be met.

Chapter 78

STAFF TRAINING POLICY

The skills, knowledge and training needs come to light during the consideration of the individual application – references and during the interview. The intelligence – how quickly the person absorbs, assimilates and puts into practice – becomes apparent after induction and after a few months of working.

To understand the needs of individual staff there must be continuous appraisals, supervision, testing (theory and practice), assessments and the Performance Review Process.

To maintain an excellent reputation of the home we must ensure that the staff employed have a variety of experience, skills and knowledge within the client group.

The staff manager and care staff need to be committed to training and work satisfaction.

Induction doesn't end after the initial intensive instruction. It continues throughout one's working life. To achieve a high quality of client care staff and resident's quality meetings will be used as an open forum for discussions of matters arising. Minutes of such meetings will circulate and posted on the notice board for all to see. (The Induction Programmed will meet skills for care standards.

The proprietor is willing to provide all resources for (1) assessing the staff needs, (2) providing in-service and external training to all staff who show the enthusiasm of benefiting from these resources, (3) all staff will have the five mandatory courses: first aid, food & hygiene, health and safety, manual handling and fire safety and recommended courses in bereavement, adult protection, infection control and mental health.

In order to measure the effectiveness of the home and the staff team, the management constantly measures personal and business achievements against the aims and objectives.

All new staff employed will either have at least NVQ in Social Care. If they do not possess this qualification, it is the policy of the Home that the staff member be willing to complete this training. All senior in charge staff will be expected to train to NVQ Level 3. The Registered Manager will be trained either as a qualified nurse or NVQ Level 4 and possess RMA or an equivalent management qualification.

As direct result of investing in people, it is the proprietor's aim that whoever leaves The Warren will do so for a higher post or opportunity carrying The Warren flag, either with his group of business or elsewhere.

It pays to invest in good, reliable, hardworking and honest staff.

SKILLS FOR CARE – INDUCTION STANDARDS

The foundation standards are requirements of the Care Standards Act 2000 and is specifically linked to standards relating to training within the National Minimum Standards which state and require that:

All staff receive induction training to NTO (National Training Organisation) specification within the first 12 weeks of appointment, which equips them to meet assessed needs of the service users accommodated, as defined in their individual plan of care.

There are five foundation standards, these are:

- Understand how to apply the value base of care
- Communicate effectively

- Develop as a worker
- Recognise and respond to abuse and neglect
- Understand the experiences and particular needs of the individuals using the service

Every standard reflects a different part of a person's job. They are not a list of training they are about the employee/carer showing they have achieved a level of understanding that is required to do their job.

All new employees will be allocated a mentor to assist them to complete our Skills for Care training programme. Any training needs will be identified during staff supervision and documented to show how these can be met.

Chapter 79

VALUABLES

Residents are encouraged to give valuables to relatives or close friends for safekeeping. There is however, a safe where valuables may be deposited.

A valuable item e.g. jewelry, important documents, etc. may be given to the person in charge, this must be witnessed by another member of staff.

An entry is to be made in the 'Valuables Book' and kept in the same cupboard as the 'Petty Cash Book', any entries must be signed by the person in charge, the Resident, if possible, and a witness.

Residents must be given a receipt for each deposit made.

At each handover, the item must be checked and signed in the 'Handover Book'.

This process is to continue until the Manager, Assistant or Proprietor is available to transfer the item to the Home's main safe.

Chapter 79

VIOLENCE AND AGGRESSION

The management and modification of a resident's disturbed or aggressive behaviour is an important part of a carer's role

In order for any policy to be effective the staff require the full support of the multi-disciplinary team and all supportive community services. An adequate staffing level is required to deal effectively and therapeutically with situations as they arise.

The resident should be accommodated in a suitable environment relevant to their illness and requirements.

It is well known that the environment residents are looked after it has an effect on their behaviour, therefore, attention should be paid to room decorations, furniture, equipment, noise and cleanliness. It is important for clients to feel safe and respected within their environment.

Once the above criteria have been met they form a good baseline for managing residents and will in fact remove some of the irritating and frustrating factors that cause violent incidents.

The staff will need to have:

1. Information - A full case history and detailed care plan needs to be provided as soon as possible to give the staff as much background information about the resident as possible.

2. Observation and Investigation - Needs to be carried out to establish the resident's condition, e.g., behaviour, mental state, emotional state, physical state.

3. Assessment - Before any admissions are made, staff should make sure that the correct category is accepted. Care plans should be updated and evaluated as and when required but not left for more than one month.

4. Treatment - A clear individual resident treatment programme must be produced and maintained, including a suitable medical treatment programme.

5. Communication - All this information needs to be conveyed to the staff via staff handovers, staff meetings, etc.

It is important to form therapeutic staff/resident relationships. It must be understood that some residents relate in a more positive way to certain staff, in these cases it may be better for that member of staff to deal with a situation. There may be a danger of manipulation - staff moral must be kept high.

Consideration should be given to the use of physical contact. To touch someone's arm for example may be a provoking situation with some residents or a friendly reassuring act with others.

A verbal rebuke may diffuse a situation or cause an increase in aggressive behaviour in others.

Large numbers of staff may help a resident to calm down or may provoke him/her into further action. The home should be adequately staffed at all times.

Male/female staff - A member of the opposite sex may have a calming therapeutic effect on the resident, or may antagonise him/her and cause more aggression.

All these effects need to be considered prior to dealing with a resident and the carer who knows an individual resident well and has a good staff/resident relationship is in the position of being able to assess a situation more accurately and decide an appropriate course of action. Discuss with other members of staff how each particular case should be tackled.

The staff need to be truthful in their dealings with residents. If a resident were to find out that he/she has been told a lie, he/she will lose all confidence in the staff members. Residents should not be misled.

It is important to discuss with the resident, aspects of his treatment and why things are done a certain way. If he/she is worried and anxious about anything he/she will require reassurance which will need to be given in calm, confident and objective manner.

The carer's attitude to the resident has an important effect on how a resident respond - the resident must be accepted as an individual and as a person in need.

In dealing with a resident who you have anticipated may become disturbed, he/she may respond to a friendly but firm approach. The skill of being able to divert this type of resident with something that may interest him is very important.

Always try to establish the reason for his/her disturbed behaviour. It may be something simple like - no cigarettes, money, an expected visitor not arriving, domestic worries regarding his/her family.

In dealing with a resident it is advisable not to use threats or to say something is going to be done when you haven't got the authority to ensure it is carried out.

Consider channelling resident's aggression through activities, e.g., games, occupational therapy, physical exercise, walking. Prevent boredom.

Never show hostility or threaten residents and do not show resentment or indifference.

If possible, leave a situation to quieten down and then approach the resident.

Prevention

When interviewing a potentially violent resident in an office or side room, remove any objects, i.e. ashtrays, ornaments, bottles, which may be used as a weapon.

Some elderly confused or mentally ill clients can exhibit aggression and their behaviourist reactions as a result causes required knowledge and skill to manage aggression and therefore redeem the risk of injury to the residence and the bystanders.

WHAT TO DO:

Staff caring for people who have the potential to be either physically violent or abusive should be recommended

1. Not to be confrontational
2. Not to take personal offences as the result or accusation
3. Not to raise their voices
4. Not to attempt to lead away the confused person or initiate any other form of physical contact, as such actions can be easily misunderstood and resented – it may be appropriate to lead the resident away from the aggressive person.
5. Not to approach the resident rapidly
6. Not to approach the resident from behind

7. Not to corner the confused resident as this will heighten feelings of threat and alarm

8. Not to crowd them by calling for assistance from several members of staff

9. Not to use restraint – see additional policy/procedures

10. Not to show alarm, anxiety or fear or this can either encourage people to become more violent or agitate them.

RECOMMENDED PRACTICE WHEN DEALING WITH AGGRESSION

1. Stay calm

2. Respect their personal space, this does vary from person to person, but generally in times of stress a distance of 2 feet may be indicated. Keep a safe distance and allow the person to remain in their present position, in general give the resident plenty of room.

3. Provide reassurance that they will not be harmed.

4. If appropriate, (or possible) ask indirect other people to keep back and not to interfere.

5. Encourage them to talk rather than they act out their anger.

6. Ask the resident what is frustrating them, try to discover the reason for their actions, but try to ensure that they understand that this is not acceptable behaviour

7. Listen to complaints, be flexible and accepting, not rigid and rejecting

8. Provide alternatives to the behaviour, or divert their attention

9. If they have a good relationship with one of the staffs let them take charge of the situation

10. Once the resident begins to calm down try to engage the resident in casual conversation, quiet and private away from the rest of the residents.

11. Remember, approach the resident in a calm, open manner and speak in a clear, calm and controlled manner to reduce further risk of aggression.

12. Staff who are worried about dealing with aggressive and confused residents should be encouraged to openly discuss their feelings.

13. If the client does not have an appointed mental health medic, notify the G.P. and request a referral

14. If staff are unable to diffuse the situation and feel themselves or others may come to harm they should call 999 and ask for police assistance.

15. If a client exhibits physical aggression towards other clients or staff this must be recorded in the Incident Book and the local CSCI office notified.

16. An incident form must be completed. If the client has a C.P.N. and a care manager they must also be notified. The person you spoke to and time must be written in the care notes and the incident book. If they do not have a C.P.N. then the duty care manager of the placing authority e.g. Croydon, Bromley or Richmond must be notified ensuring you record the person's name and time of call.

17. All incidents of violence must be reported to C.S.C.I. (recording the name and time again in the incident book and care notes).

18. Report of GP and if client doesn't have a psychiatrist request a referral back to one.

Record feedback from G.P. in documents above.

19. Notify the care manager or the duty care manager of the placing authority

20. Notify next of kin

21. If the behaviour of the resident becomes such that it cannot be managed, then the GP, psychiatrist or next of kin and other relevant professionals must be made aware of the situation and a review of the care plan made.

Chapter 80

VISITORS

'Open House' is the policy towards visitors to the home. The home encourages relatives, friends and other i.e. voluntary organisations etc., to visit the home during the day. This enables visitors to come along when it is convenient to them and encourages stimulation for the service users.

The Home encourages clients to maintain contact with relatives and friends within the community, participation in their care will be encouraged unless the client objects.

Visitors are welcome between 9.00 am and 9.00 pm. If a visitor wishes to see a resident after 9.00 pm, they are requested to telephone the home prior to visiting for security purposes.

Visitors are able to go into Service Users rooms. Arrangements will be made clear at the outset to both visitors and Service Users in order to avoid and prevent awkward situations between staff and visitors.

Some visitors may not like to sit and talk with their relatives or friends in a public room, this is especially the case if a Service User is hard of hearing and they are required to shout. If it is possible the ideal is to set apart a room private use, however if this is not possible the Service Users own room can be used.

Visitors are welcome to participate in our annual barbecue in June and our Christmas Party. They are also encouraged to participate and raise comments, which will be discussed at Residents' Meetings, which are held three monthlies. The date of these meetings will be displayed on the residents' noticeboard.

Comments and suggestions are welcomed, and a box is kept on the ground floor hallway at the home, which is emptied weekly and if possible, your comments will be actioned. At six monthly intervals, we will send out questionnaires to gather comments on the Home. Your participation on completing these is welcomed.

Visitors may enter bedrooms with clients consent. Smoking is restricted to the designated smoking area.

Visitors are reminded that they are expected to not exhibit disruptive behaviour to our clients or staff.

Children remain the responsibility of responsible adult visitor.

All visitors must ring the doorbell for admittance and will be greeted by a staff member. The visitor will be asked to confirm who they are, whom they are visiting. The visitors' book must be signed so that if there is a fire, there is a record of who is in the home.

Official visitors must produce identification before being admitted into the home. Official visitors must also sign the visitors' book.

Chapter 81

VISITS AND REPORTS
BY REGISTERED PERSON(S) OF A HOME
Regulation 26 of National Care Standards

THE REGULATION – and associated conditions:

Visits by person in control of the home

Where the person in control of the home is not also the manager of the home he shall at least once in every moth visit the home or arrange for another person to visit the home on his behalf and report in writing to him on the conduct of the home.

Where the person in control of the home is a company, society, association or other body or firm, the directors or other persons responsible for the management of the body or the partners of the firm shall arrange for one or more of their number to visit the home at least once in every month and to report in writing to them on the conduct of the home.

The Regulation clearly distinguishes between the registered person and a company, society, association or other body or firm in control; the abiding rule is, therefore, that ANY home which has a separate manager appointed in charge of it MUST be formally visited at least once in every month. Such measure will be for the benefit and protection of both the person in charge and the manager, evidencing their responsible approach to the management of the home.

Homes with a vacancy for the managers post (i.e. where a manager has recently left the post) or where a home is undergoing the recruitment of a manager to the post (and is therefore awaiting a registration interview and hence the manager is yet to be registered), MUST continue to comply with the regulation by the monthly visit being conducted with the nominated person in day to day charge of the home at the time.

This Regulation only does not apply where the person in control owns and directly manages the home on a day to day basis. This would be recognised on the Certificate of Registration.

In such circumstances, the person in control will only be expected to manage one establishment and sufficient active management hours must be devoted to the home to ensure its smooth and efficient running.

The person in charge in this situation should still conduct adequate monitoring of the service provided and maintain proper records of this. This will consist of a monthly 'audit' or a 'quality check' which evaluates the quality and standard of care. Documents such as the Social Services Inspectorate's books such as 'Homes are for Living In' or their 'Caring for Quality' series include formats for such audits.

THE VISIT

As a matter of good practice, [and to comply with the 'spirit or Regulation 9(3)] the visit by the person in control monitoring the home should include that person independently touring the building, meeting with residents and staff and viewing records and documents as they may so require. The visit should seek to include an examination of the following elements:

1. Residents' wellbeing, stimulation and comfort
2. Food provided – its adequacy, quality and availability
3. Occupancy levels
4. Staffing – development and other issues

413

5.   Health & Safety issues – Fire precautions/Hygiene/Risk Assessments
6.   Premises issues – cleanliness and maintenance
7.   Management issues – complaints and supervision arrangement

All inspections / audits are 'useless' without discussion between the person in control and the manager of both outcomes from previous visits, and the setting of 'action plans' for the future; visits such as that suggested above must have clear 'feedback' time to the manager, and the decisions arrived at must be agreed and *clearly recorded.*

THE REPORT

It is recommended that a standard format is devised by the home which can act as a checklist as well as allowing the detail to be filled in at the time of the visit.

As a matter of good practice, the Report should include – as well as taking into aspects of the above suggested 'visit' areas:

1.   Name of the person visiting, date & time of visit
2.   A simple description of the visit (which staff/residents seen, which parts of the home visited, etc.)

3. Issues / outcomes from previous visit's action plan

4. A list of the records examined / audited during the visit

5. Issues raised by the person in control

6. Issues brought to attention of the person in control by the manager

7. Action plan for the month ahead [and further where necessary]

Reports should be preferably completed at the time of the visit, be signed by both parties, and duplicated to ensure that both parties have an immediate copy of the outcomes of the visit to keep, consider and action.

The Visit Reports must be kept within the home at all times to comply with Regulation 6 and be available for inspection by any person so authorised to do so by the registering authority.

Chapter 82

VOLUNTEERS

It is the homes policy to allow residents to accept volunteers who come from a recognised reputable agency, to make sure the volunteer has been vetted. The acceptance of volunteers may be beneficial, especially to residents who have no visitors or contacts.

RESTRICTIONS TO VOLUNTARY WORKERS
The voluntary worker must not carry out any personal attention e.g. personal care, toileting, bathing without both the residents/advocate and managers approval.

JOBS WHICH VOLUNTARY WORKERS MAY DO
Escort residents to the shops, church, hospital, outings, spend time with the residents.
Any outings requiring transportation should be approved by the manager. (Volunteers car must be checked for insurance, MOT and tax).
All volunteers are subject to having an enhanced (CRB (criminal record bureau) check, which is free, and two-character references.

Chapter 83

Unpredictable behaviour

The unpredictability of the behaviour of some people creates a great deal of stress for many staff. Much of our skill in handling 'normal' everyday aggressive situations derives from our ability to think our way creatively into the minds of our upset or angry patients or relatives. Since our respective realities have many points in common, we can often be surprisingly accurate in our assessment of what the matter is and how best to manage the situation. However, when we are confronted with people whose realities are substantially different from ours, e.g. the mentally ill, a drunk, a drug addict, a confused elderly person, etc., we may feel we have no points of contact or communication; it can feel that we are left helpless, totally unaided by our 'normal' skills. Negotiations become an extremely limited option – how do you negotiate with someone who is 'on a different planet?

The trouble is that it is more than not a case of hit and miss. Staff working for mentally ill patients will often find the right words and actions that will help to calm a disturbed patient. However, these same words and actions will probably have no effect on another disturbed patient, nor may they be particularly helpful for other staff. Obviously the better you know your patients, the safer you are likely to be, for you will have had opportunities perhaps to find windows of rationality or contact in their disturbance through which you can more clearly communicate.

Such is the situation with many mentally ill and disturbed persons whose behaviour we cannot predict with any accuracy. If we experience a sudden eruption of aggression and violence, often we are left with no option but to look for escape and to remove others to safety, or to take steps to protect ourselves and others. Physical restraint may be a possibility in extreme situations where, for example, real injury to someone is imminent and there is no means of escape; even then, it should never be attempted unless the member of staff is strong enough to succeed and knows how it can be applied safely.

Even innocent actions on the part of such people can create a state of arousal in staff. For example, imagine the scenario; an obviously mentally ill person wanders from the waiting room into the internal reception office; he closes the door and stands against it staring at the receptionist's back; she becomes aware of his stare, turns round to look and panics with fear. Is the receptionist in danger or not? Her problem is that she cannot trust any of the cues in the situation which she would have been able to do with a 'normal' person, e.g. Facial expression, eyes, posture, previous experience of the person, etc. finding nothing in the situation to reassure her of her safety, she becomes afraid. It is not that the signs are suggesting danger; rather it is that they are suggesting 'normality'.

Why do we feel embarrassed or unhappy when we are confronted with the behaviour of certain types of people? For example:

- The bizarre behaviour of the person who is obviously suffering from a psychotic mental illness, who hears voices, or who responds in odd ways;
- The drunk who starts talking to us, holding on for support
- The drug addict or solvent sniffers who make wild threats

- The confused elderly person who thinks we are someone from his youth
- The gang of youths whom we might find quite frightening when we meet them on an estate;
- Very angry people, who are obviously out of control

With normal everyday behaviour, we can predict a great deal, we say 'hello' and we expect someone to say 'hello' back. There are many social conventions that all 'normally' behaving people comply with; If I enter a waiting room with many empty chairs and in which you are already sitting, unless I know you I will sit with at least one empty chair between us; if we are strangers, then I don't expect you to come up and hug me, etc.

Being able to predict gives us a certain measure of control over situations; if we have a fair idea of what is going to happen, then we feel more in control. Herein lies our problem with unpredictable behaviour- we don't feel in control. How can we negotiate when we don't feel we understand what is going on? How can we play any game if we don't know the rules. How can we negotiate with someone if we can't get inside their head. Thus we become embarrassed, or uncomfortable, or unhappy, and ultimately we feel threatened.

- Although we know we should not stereotype, we would be foolish if we did not learn the lesson of precious experience with a patient, a family, a neighbourhood or a block of flats. Never ignore any patient's history of upsetting or dangerous behaviour on the grounds that it was a long time ago or that they promised to turn over a new leaf.

- When you become aware that someone is behaving unpredictably, think 'defensively', i.e. think more about yourself and your safety than the job you are supposed to be doing at the time; go on full alert immediately. If you are wrong or if things settle back to normal, you can then relax and give more attention to the job in hand.

- Trust your intuition; it may be the only warning you get that something is not quite as it should be. Remember that men have intuition as well as women; it is probably called women's intuition because women appear to trust it more than men. It is certainly difficult to justify your concerns to a superior on the basis of intuition and we can be left feeling somewhat exposed to criticism as we try to explain that we did what we did because of a 'feeling'. Despite this difficulty, our intuition should be trusted.

- If ever there was a time to keep your distance, this is it; the incident with the knife at someone's throat would not have happened if the aggressor had not got close enough. If the door from the waiting-room to the reception office had been locked, no one could have wandered in.

- Be sure you are aware of where the exit s and that you have as easy access to it as possible. Give some thought, prior to any incident occurring , to any alternative exit, e.g. Could a receptionist escape from someone within the reception office by climbing over the reception counter?

- Don't become too absorbed in your job; it may be important that you keep an eye on where people are, what they are doing, what potential weapons are about, etc. Hence the advantage of a colleagues company; he or she can be monitoring the safety aspects while you can be getting on with the job, or vice versa.

- Be prepared to call for help in any way possible. Panic buttons need to be checked to ensure they work – and also that other staff know how to respond when they go off; a loud shout or scream would be better practised first to check that you can be heard; a screech alarm or cordless doorbell are considering; as a last resort, you can always throw something through the window, e.g. The fire extinguisher.

- Ultimately, be prepared to leave when you feel you are not sufficiently in control. It need not be an admission of defeat to leave if you feel you have to do so for your safety' s sake; remember Strangeways Prison in 1991- the whole prison service, hundreds of them, well-trained and with the best of safety equipment, pulled out and let the prisoners wreck the prison.

CHAPTER 84

VULNERABLE

What Is A "Vulnerable" Adult?

- Legally, an "adult" is any person aged 18 or over ▪ "Vulnerability" arises where there may be a difficulty in the adult's ability to make a fully informed judgement for themselves ▪ Any adult capable of being hurt physically, emotionally or in any other way is, therefore, a "vulnerable adult". ▪ Any adult who may not be fully able to entirely protect themselves from harm or being taken advantage of, in any way, is a "vulnerable adult".

Who Might abuse Someone?

- In care environments, the most obvious person who might abuse someone is a person who cares for an adult that is vulnerable ▪In a care home, a Service User might abuse another Service User where one of them is more able than the other▪ A colleague might abuse another colleague

There are a large number of people in a position of power or influence over others who might abuse, for example: ▪Carers ▪Friends▪ Health Workers ▪Managers ▪ Owners ▪ Relatives ▪ Service Users ▪ Staff ▪ Supervisors ▪Visitors ▪ Volunteers

Defining "Abuse", the best ways to understand what abuse is are: ▪ Where a person in authority, power and/or trust uses that position to impair the wellbeing of another person in some way ▪ The ill treatment of another person ▪ Where a person violates the rights of another person ▪ That abuse could be rare, occasional or regular

Abuse could be: ▪ Deliberate or unintentional ▪ Through negligence ▪ Through ignorance
Patterns of Abuse ▪ Opportunism, for example, the theft of something left lying around ▪ Situation, for example, becoming exasperated by the difficulties that arises when caring for someone with particular difficulties such as, say, challenging behaviour ▪ Institutional, for example, lack of proper care standards in a care home environment ▪ Unacceptable practices, for example, withholding food or isolating someone ▪ Misappropriation, for example, using someone's benefits or money ▪ Fraud, for example,

inappropriately influencing someone's will or assets.

Types of Abuse

Seven general types of abuse encountered in care environment are: ▪Physical abuse ▪Sexual abuse ▪Emotional abuse ▪Financial abuse ▪Institutional abuse ▪Discriminatory abuse▪ Neglect

Remember, any one of these could be: ▪Deliberate or unintentional ▪Through negligence ▪Through ignorance

Types of Physical Abuse

Physical abuse represents 56% of known abuse in care environments. It includes: ▪Depriving someone ▪ Hitting ▪Inappropriate medication ▪Kicking ▪Pushing ▪ Restraint (certain types of) ▪ Slapping

Types of Sexual Abuse

Sexual abuse represents 10% of known abuse in care environments. In learning disability environments, the problem may be two to three times worse. It includes: ▪ Inappropriate photography ▪ Inappropriate sexual stimulation ▪ Inappropriate touching ▪ Pressuring someone into a sexual act ▪ Rape ▪ Sexual assault

Types of Emotional Abuse

Emotional abuse represents 4% of known abuse in care environments. It includes: ▪ Blaming ▪ Bullying ▪ controlling ▪Deprivation ▪ Humiliation ▪ Intimidating ▪ Isolation ▪ Name Calling ▪ Shouting ▪ Swearing ▪ Threats ▪ Verbal abuse

Types of Financial Abuse

Financial abuse represents 10% of known abuse in care environments. It includes: ▪ Exploitation ▪ Fraud ▪ Mismanaging possessions, benefits etc. ▪ Mismanaging Service users finances ▪ Pressuring someone into financial transactions ▪ Pressuring someone into giving gifts, legacies (wills) etc ▪ Pressuring someone into material transactions ▪ Theft

Types of Institutional Abuse

This includes:

▪ Caring in a way to suit the care provider rather than the Service user ▪ Impinging upon someone's rights ▪ Inability of Service User to use the 'phone privately ▪ Lack of privacy ▪ Limiting choice ▪ Opening Service User's private mail

Much institutional abuse is to do with the "tone", the "feel", the "way we do things" whereby the care provider "sets the agenda" to suit the needs of the manager, staff etc, rather than "setting the agenda" specifically to suit the needs of the Service User.

Types of Discriminatory Abuse

Abuse Statistics

It is well known that the reported abuse is the tip of the iceberg- much more goes on than people report formally. You will often hear people say, "well, we shouldn't really do that, but…"

This is not acceptable, if you know it shouldn't be happening, it shouldn't be happening!

Over 50% of known abuse is physical, yet on 4% of known abuse is emotional.

1. In your experience, are carers more likely to hit, deprive a Service User or are they more likely to "bad mouth", threaten a Service User?

2. If they are more likely to "bad mouth", threaten is a physical or emotional abuse?

3. Therefore, why do you think we know about more physical abuse happening than we do about emotional abuse happening?
4. Which is worse- physical abuse or emotional abuse?

Responses:

1. More carers say they have experienced Service Users being "bad mouthed" or threatened than they have experienced Service Users being hit or physically deprived.
2. This means more carers have experienced emotional abuse than they have experienced physical abuse of Service Users.
3. It is probable that, far more emotional abuse exists than physical abuse. Yet, we know about more physical abuse than emotional abuse because there is the idea that "physical abuse is worse".
4. Neither physical or emotional abuse is worse than other (or any other type of

abuse), they are all as bad and all as unacceptable.

Neglect by others

Neglect is NOT:

•merely an oversight ▪ a touch of bad practice ▪ "she'll just have to wait"

Neglect is;

▪ something not happening when it should ▪ ignoring a person's needs ▪ a failure to provide for that person ▪ either intentional or unintentional ▪ both physical and/ or emotional ▪ a specific form of abuse

As a care provider, is it right to fall short (in any way) of doing just that – providing care when it should be provided as it should be provided.

Physical Neglect

Physical neglect has two main categories:

▪ Lack of something ▪ Not helping someone

Lack of something could include:

•shortage of food ▪ lack of attention ▪ inadequate medication ▪ not enough light ▪ insufficient warmth

Not helping something could include:

▪ Not helping them dress properly ▪ not helping them move safely ▪ leaving them unshaven ▪ not helping them wash, bathe properly ▪ letting them wet themselves

Emotional Neglect

Includes:

- confining someone
- ignoring someone
- isolating someone
- keeping someone "out of the way".

Chapter 85

WHISTLE BLOWING POLICY

The purpose of this procedure is to protect our staff and vulnerable clients. All staff must be aware of their responsibilities to others.

Any staff member who has witnessed or been told by another member of staff or client that abuse, theft or anything that may potentially cause harm to the client, management or home he/she must report the incident immediately to the Manager or person on call. However, staff members can also contact the CSCI directly if you are concerned with a matter concerning the management or proprietor.

A written statement must also be made with full details of the occurrence. Failure to report these incidences will be seen as aiding and abetting the incident and therefore the disciplinary procedure will be used. The police and CSCI will be notified if an incident comes to light at a later stage and was not reported to the management.

Staff have to whistle blow, if they observe or are aware of poor practice or negligence is being practiced and will not be penalised or discriminated against. Any staff found not to whistle blow will be classed as aiding and abetting.

Staff will be protected by the home as regards to confidentiality – only people who need to know (e.g. police, CSCI will be advised) of any statements or actions.

Chapter 86

Religion

Every Service User has the right to continue to attend a place of worship of his or her faith; Staff in the home will ensure that this is possible. Staff transport, relatives or volunteers may be used for this purpose. If the Service User is incapable of attending their chosen place of worship, then ministers should be invited to hold services in the home and encouraged to converse with other Service Users who may not be of their religion.

Considerable comfort is often gained from faith in declining years, even with people who have had little to do with their faith since their childhood. It is an important part of the life and routine of the home and many Service Users benefit from conversation with people connected with religious organisations. This can be arranged through client's request. The home will facilitate the observance of these religious festivals that are appropriate to the faith of the residents living within the home.

The observance of religious rituals to be carried out prior and post death is assured.

Chapter 87

Other support for service user

Equipment

- The home should have access to pressure-relieving equipment from medical loans. This is used when a Service Users Assessment indicates its need. District Nurses can also provide additional equipment when necessary.

Activities

Service Users need to lead fulfilled lives; a stimulating, interesting activities programme is on offer in the home.

Service Users must be involved in the activities programme through consultation and the programme must be amended to accommodate their changing wishes. Mobility and disabilities are to be considered. We have a visiting music therapist and aromatherapist, which is enjoyed by many residents.

Service Users need to live ordinary and as far as possible independent lives and the activities programme should be able to support this objective. They need to be able to remain involved in activities that interested them before they moved into residential care. There may be some Service Users, who due to their loss of mental or physical ability may not be able to continue to enjoy the activities they had done previously. The aim of the activities programme in this case will be to introduce them to other activities that will open up new areas of interest and provide the ongoing stimulation they need. An activity rota for the month is displayed on the residents' notice board.

Chapter 88

Service Users Meetings

This must be held every 3 months; minutes are kept on file.

The objectives of Service User Meeting:

- Residents meetings should give the residents an opportunity to comment on the operation of the home.
- Matters of concern can be raised.
- Contributions and suggestions for inclusion in the activities in the home.
- Management can use the meetings to inform the service users of impending events, new policies, and changes taking place in the home and to gain the views of the group.

Chapter 89

OUR 11-POINT COMMUNICATIONS

We are always looking for new and improved ways to keep communication channels open among our employees. We want you to feel free to tell us about your personal recommendations for improvements and any problems you may be experiencing on the job.

The following 11-Point Communication Programme summarises many of the ways you can share your ideas and concerns with us.

First: Employee Induction. The first part of our programme is conducted by the Manager to help you adjust to your new working environment by providing information about such matters as prospective proprietor benefits, wages, disciplinary procedures, promotional opportunities, safety and security. When you report to your assigned job, the Manager will review specific rules, regulations and practices within the home.

Second: Informal communications Between You and Manager/Proprietor. If you have any questions concerning your job or job-related activities, your Manager should be the first person to talk to. This is always the best place to start when you have a work-related concern. If, however, you do not feel comfortable discussing a particular matter with your Manager, be assured that the other methods of communications discussed here are available to you also.

Third: Our "Problem-Solving" Procedure. During the performance of your duties, questions or problems may arise or personal problems may occur that affect your work. The following procedure has been established for your use in resolving these matters:

Step 1.   Talk to your Manager about the problem.

Step 2.   If your Manager cannot resolve your problem to your satisfaction within three business days, ask for a meeting with the Proprietor to talk it over.

Step 3.   If the Proprietor cannot resolve your problem to your satisfaction within three business days, ask for a meeting with the Registration Officer.

Step 4.   If the Registration Officer cannot resolve your problem to your satisfaction within three business days, talk it over with the Citizens' Advice Bureau.

NOTE: If the problem is of such a nature that you wish to remain anonymous, you may send a letter to the Proprietor, who will review it and take appropriate action.

We believe this procedure will ensure that your problem will be thoroughly reviewed.   In any emergency situation, the "Step" time periods can be speeded up if you request.

We recognise that some problems may be either of a very personal nature or that, for some other good reason, you may prefer not to discuss the matter with your Manager. In such a case, you should consult the Home for advice as to how to handle the situation. Above all remember that we cannot help you solve your problems if you do not tell us about them.

Fourth: Informal Discussions Between Manager and Small Groups of_Employees. The manager meets with employees in small groups in order to hear any concerns that you want to raise personally and to update you on developments within The Home . These informal sessions will be held on a regular basis, and you have our pledge to answer the questions you raise at these sessions – or find the answers if we do not already know them.

Fifth: Employee Survey. Because your opinions matter to us at The Home , we want to give you the opportunity to communicate with us about all aspects of the facilities and your work here. To be sure your opinions are being heard, we periodically conduct a survey. Your responses to questions in these surveys are confidential. From the surveys we learn from you what our strong points are. We also learn about areas that need improvement, both in specific sections and The Home . Top management responds to, and in many cases makes changes, as a result of suggestions that you make. We encourage you to participate in these surveys because your cooperation is vital to their success.

Sixth: Problems. As particular problems or questions come to the attention of The Home , we may appoint a team composed of Manager/Proprietor/Legal Representative/Cook/Senior Staff to review specific issues regarding the problem or question and to make recommendations to The Home . When appropriate, our belief is that these teams will enable us to gain a cross-section of views and obtain mutually satisfactory solutions to problems that our employees are uniquely qualified to investigate.

Seventh: Suggestions' Boxes. This is another way of letting us know about suggestions or questions. In the Home there is a Suggestion Box for this purpose. As described previously, the Suggestion Committee reviews suggestions and forwards them to the appropriate person for evaluation. An award is offered to the person who suggests is implemented. You do not have to disclose your name if you prefer not to. However, putting your name on your suggestion gives us an opportunity to ask you for more information and it gives you an opportunity to be eligible for an award.

Eighth: Noticeboard: This is used mainly for the residents' benefit.

Ninth: Employee Bulletin Boards: You will notice the bulletin boards at each facility. The purpose of these boards is to communicate changes in The Home policy, news or job vacancies and other information of concern to you. These bulletin boards, therefore, are to be used only for communications from The Home to you. You are expected to glance at the bulletin boards each day to read any new material posted there.

Tenth: Benefits' Session: We believe that it is very important to keep you informed of the benefits in The Home Circle of Security, and their value, in order to enable you to better plan for your future financial security. From time to time, therefore, a representative of our Insurance Carrier will be meeting with you either individually or in small groups to inform you of your prospective proprietor benefits/other insurance and to answer your questions about their value. You will need to request this meeting, which the Management will be happy to arrange.

Eleventh: Employee Groups: As an employee, you may be provided the opportunity from time-to-time to serve on any of several teams which have been set to promote the general interests of all employees.

These include:
1. Client Welfare Team:
 2. Client Support Team;
3. Client Advocate: Deputy Manager for Dementia and Mental Health.

Affirmative Action Team: The purpose of this team is to actively pursue an affirmative action programme by developing and executing plans designed to encourage the growth of ethnic and minority employees and residents at The   Home and to communicate this programme to employees, residents and the community at large.

The In-Service Education Team: This team assesses needs and develops plans for comprehensive educational programs for employees of all of The Home 's facilities. Its purpose is to provide employees with a full range of training in job related subjects. Programmes are also geared to general subjects, such as safety, understanding the elderly, sanitation, etc.

The Policy is made up of prospective proprietor volunteers who have an interest in news gathering and writing articles.

The Recreation and Activities Team plans, develops and coordinates recreational programmes and activities to be enjoyed by employees and residents.

Safety Team promotes an effective safety programme to reduce and minimise accidental injuries. The team makes recommendations on how to avoid injury and what safety precautions to take on the job.

The Suggestion Team is designed to promote and encourage employees to participate in The Home s affairs by making constructive suggestions.

Volunteers are needed to serve on each of the above teams. If you wish to volunteer, please see your Manager.

To sum up, we believe this 11-Point Communications Program will give you such a variety of opportunities to communicate with us that you should have no problems or concerns left unexpressed or unanswered. Please take advantage of any or all of these lines of communication to help us maintain The Home s as an excellent place to work.

Chapter 90

BULLYING

This can either be physical or emotional and is regarded as abuse.

The Management will not tolerate bullying amongst residents or the staff.

Residents who bully others must be discouraged by staff.

An urgent review will be held with the Presence of the Care Manager, CPN and relatives. Persistent bullying may result in the Management asking the client to find an alternative Home. Staff who bullies clients or other staff, either physically or verbally will be dealt with through the Home's Disciplinary Procedure.

Chapter 91

ALCOHOL AND SUBSTANCE ABUSE

Staff

Staff must not turn up for work if they are under the influence of alcohol and or illegal substances and indulge whilst on duty, visit the premises when off duty.

Staff must inform management if they are/can take any ex medication which is being taken whilst on duty.

Residents

May drink alcohol but not in excessive amounts in which may be a danger to themselves or others. Staff will advise and record the client's consumption of alcohol. Staff will liaise with the Doctor or N.O.K. or care management, if persistent alcohol abuse continuing.

Persistent alcohol abuse leading to danger to yourself or others may result to a termination of your contract.

Illegal Substances

This is not allowed under any circumstances on the premises. Residents must be aware that if they are found in possession or found using illegal substances the management have been obliged to inform the police and the C.S.C.I

Visitors

Visitors are not allowed on the premises when they are under the influence of alcohol or abusing illegal substances. Visitors are not allowed to bring any kind of illegal substance to the home.

Chapter 92

TAKEN CLIENT HISTORY

DATE OF BIRTH:

PLACE OF BIRTH:

FAMILY: parents - occupation, date of death
            married life
            children - names &
            ages   family
            contacts
            brothers & sisters - names -
            whether they are alive and where
            they live - address

SCHOOL: name and location
            age started and finished school
            academic qualifications professional
            qualifications   favoured   sports
            friends
            likes and dislikes at school e.g.
            teachers, subjects

EMPLOYMENT: age started, place
            of work position
            what the work involved hours
            how long in each job pay
            retirement from work

EXPERIENCES: most   important   or   unusual

experience

they will never forget

HOBBIES: favourite hobbies at work, school,
              retirement, pets
   TRAAVEL: countries   visited   or   holiday
destinations

SOCIAL LIFE: cinema, theatre, drinking, smoking,
              gambling things they've enjoyed
              doing

PERSONALITY: introvert, extrovert

LLNESS: diagnosis
PHYSICAL :   major illness, hospital, operations
MENTAL: illness resulting, hospital

              admission. Senses - sight

              Hearing, smell

Admitted to the home, Background to admission

Family Friends

References

Will It Fly? by Thomas K. McKnight. One of the biggest questions …

Lucky Or Smart? by Bo Peabody. Bo Peabody was an Internet …

The Fire Starter Sessions by Danielle LaPorte. If you've been timid about …

Million Dollar Consulting by Alan Weiss. Million Dollar Consulting is what …

From Birth to life years 4th edn by Ajay Sharma & Helen Cockenhil

Energetic Boundaries by Clydi Dale

This is going to hurt by Adam Kay

Netter's Anatomy flash cards by John. T. Hansen

The Subtle Body by Christine Northirup.MD

Nursing practice

The obesity Code by Dr. Johnson Fung

Index

Made in the USA
Las Vegas, NV
28 January 2022

42490740R00252